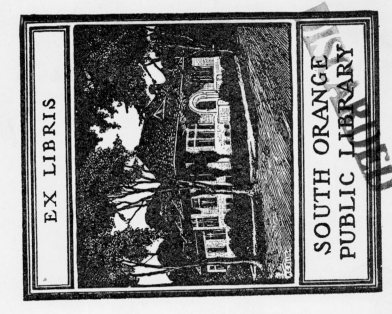

THE VELVET BUBBLE

The
Velvet Bubble

by ALICE WINTER

William Morrow & Co.
NEW YORK, 1965

cpy 1

for

Alex Cappon, University of Missouri at Kansas City
Frances Grinstead, University of Kansas Writers' Conference

Chapter 1

➷ ➷ ➷ ➷ ➷ ➷ ➷ ➷ ➷ ➷ ➷ ➷ ➷ ➷

I was fourteen years old, and for ages every time Mrs. Berkson saw me she said, "My, how she's growing up," but now, because I had just become half an orphan, she came and put her arms around me and muttered, "Poor child, poor child."

Women from the church were in the kitchen and relatives were all over the place, and I went out in the back yard, as far away as I could get from the confusion. I dragged the old wicker chair across the lawn to the other side of the spiraea bushes, clear out of sight of the house.

I had a book with me, and it was a good one, but I felt too peaceful to get interested in it again. I just sat there feeling the soft, warm air on my skin and smelling the yellow tea roses that grew along the garage. I had never had such a warm, safe feeling. I felt as though there were velvet cushions all around me, making things easy.

An ant crawled up the wicker chair, clear to the arm where my hand rested. Usually I killed every ant or any other kind of insect that came my way, but now I wouldn't have hurt this ant for anything, I loved it. The great peace I felt made me love it. I loved everything—the sunshine and the roses and the cottonwood leaves, each dancing its separate dance. Even the ugly old fence across the alley around the Berkson place looked beautiful to me.

I looked up, and Aunt Helen was coming across the grass at me. As usual, she walked as though she knew exactly where she was going, how many steps it would take, and precisely what she would do when she got there. Through the spiraea bushes I watched her bearing down on me. She had on the spike heels she was always wears, and I could imagine the trail of little holes she was leaving in the lawn. Her peroxide hair, which should have been dark like mine, was stiff with lacquer. The little breeze didn't disturb a single hair. I saw a tornado come and leave everything—me and the roses and the ant—undisturbed but blow her hair until the lacquer was powerless and the short yellow hairs blew straight out from her face, and then the tornado got stronger and blew off her head and only the dark-green dress and the legs were coming at me.

"There you are, Dorrie, darling," she said, and I knew that as she came toward me she had been deciding which word to accent, going over the sentence in her mind, trying out the different possibilities, and coming up with the one that best suited her dramatic sense.

I gave her a half-smile which seemed proper and said, "Hi, Aunt Helen."

"You shouldn't run off grieving by yourself like this," she said. "It isn't good for you."

I closed the smile off my face and she came over and put her arm around my shoulder. Her left hand was right in front of my eyes and I saw how old-looking it was with the veins sticking out and the skin parched with a thousand tiny wrinkles. There was a faint lilac scent on it, from hand cream, I thought, but her hands were past help. She stood there leaning over me, smoothing back my hair. "Poor baby, poor baby," she moaned, and I thought she was wasting a good performance on an audience of one.

She straightened up and said, "Come on in, honey. We've got to pick out what you'll wear to the funeral."

Even the force of her personality couldn't erase the good feeling I had. As I walked with her into the house and up to my room, it stayed with me, enfolding me like a soft, protective cloud.

My room is yellow and white because it's on the north side—that had been their idea. Sometimes the cheerfulness of it had been an insult to me, but now I felt as though it were filled with sunshine. One thing I learned a long time ago is you can't help how you feel. People can say do this, do that, stand up straight, practice your piano, play with other children, and most of the time you're helpless as a robot. But you're not a robot, and you've got feelings, and no one can control them.

All Aunt Helen had to do was look once through my closet. She reached in and took out the gray shirtwaist dress, maybe because it was the closest to black. With her usual certainty of being right she said, "This would be best, Dorrie," and she hung it on the duck lamp.

"Now what about shoes? Are your white ones clean?"

Without waiting for an answer, she stooped over and took a pair of white pumps from the shoe rack, and of course they were clean and ready to wear. She went about then, opening drawers and taking out underwear, and laying it on the bureau as though I didn't know where things were. When she finished she said, "Come on downstairs now. Your grandma's here and she'd like to see you."

But I had the feeling that my thin little grandma with her sour-apple face might make the soft cloud go away from me, so I said, "I'm awfully tired, Aunt. I hardly slept at all last night. Couldn't I just rest a while?"

"I guess so, honey," she said. "I'll tell her you'll be down later."

She went out and made a big thing of being quiet about closing the door. I lay on my bed and pulled my Teddy bear over to me and rubbed the worn spot on his ear. I looked up at the gray dress hanging against the wall and thought of all the trouble it had caused when I bought it. There was some irony in the fact that I'd had to fight to get it and now Aunt Helen picked it for me to wear to the funeral. She couldn't have pleased me more.

I thought of the next day and wondered if my classmates would be at the church. If it had been during the school year, they would have taken up a collection for flowers. That's what we did when we were in fourth grade and Elvira Simmons' father died. And then when she came back to school the following Monday, we treated her like a queen. We let her choose the games we played and a couple of the big girls made a seat for her with their arms and carried her around. But it didn't last very long, just a day or so, and then she went back to being like anybody else. Elvira was a nobody in class except when her father died.

I wasn't the nobody Elvira was, with my father being the manager of the whole office at Galley and Sons and my mother being one of the best-looking women in town, but I knew that if any of the kids from school were at the funeral the next day, I'd look more important to them than I ever had before. Not that I'd ever cared what the kids thought. Mostly they bored me.

But now I felt more kindly even toward them. I liked everybody better. I could tell how easy being good was going to be from then on. I wasn't going to have to think any longer of the dark, evil things that had been at the back of my mind for as long as I could remember. I was the only one who had seen both sides of the life that went on in our house. Friends and relatives had seen a smooth, shining, happy surface—sun glint on water. I had seen what they saw. I could see it all through their eyes. But I saw it through my own eyes, too, and I knew the water wasn't sunlighted and shining. It was dark, and murky, and dirty.

·   ·   ·

About half an hour later there was a gentle tap on my door and Aunt Helen stuck her head in the room and said, "Are you rested now, darling? Your grandma's going home, but she wants to see you first."

I knew I might as well give up. There'd be no avoiding Grandma any longer. Downstairs, I was on my way through the living room to the den, when Mrs. Berkson stopped me and said, "You look pale, Dorrie. Don't you want a glass of milk?" I managed to get past her without eating or drinking anything.

In the den Grandma hugged me so hard it seemed she was trying to squeeze every bit of breath from my body, and I thought how ridiculous we must look with my short, little grandma almost squeezing me in two, and my chin sticking out over the top of her head.

She wasn't crying right then, but her voice sounded as though she were. She said, "Sister, come home and spend the night with me."

"Thanks, Grandma," I said, "but Mrs. Berkson's going to be here with me and I want to sleep in my own bed."

I knew that would satisfy her. She was always great for sleeping in your own bed. That was one of her rules along with, don't go out in the noonday sun, and drink three glasses of water between each meal. Read the Bible, pray, go to church, was part of it too, but no more important than the rest. She had all kinds of rules about how to live your days, and together they were her religion.

When Grandma was through hugging me, Aunt Helen took a turn, and finally the two of them left. I wandered out of the den and into the living room. For the moment it was empty, and I stood there thinking of how my life was going to be. I would spend long hours sitting in this room, reading. In the winter I would build a fire in the fireplace and sit in front of it with my feet on the hearth and read just as long as I wanted to.

No one would say, "Don't tell me you're reading again! You'd better get out in the fresh air and put some roses in those cheeks."

For a long time the two of them had kept me from knowing which one was really boss, but I'd finally figured it out. It wasn't that I wanted to be boss. It was just that I'd gotten awfully tired of being picked on all the time and being cheated out of the love that ought to be mine. Now I would have that love, and from then on it was going to be easy to be good.

Suddenly I knew why I'd been feeling so peaceful that day. The peacefulness came from the fact that I *wanted* to be good. That showed that being good was my true nature and that the times I'd been bad were forced on me. A lot of things had been forced on me. From the time I was very young, people would shake their heads and look at me and say, "She's old beyond her years." Some of them thought this was wonderful and they thought they were giving my parents a compliment. But others said it reprovingly, almost sadly. All I knew was that if I were old beyond my years, and precocious, as a couple of the teachers said, it was something that had been forced on me.

I decided to go out and sit in the wicker chair in the back yard again. On my way through the kitchen I heard the phrases I'd been hearing ever since the accident. Mrs. Ragan was standing at the counter slicing a chocolate cake, and in that baby-doll voice of hers she said, "I tell you, I still can't believe it. So full of life one day, gone the next."

It seemed as though I were the only one who didn't have trouble believing it. But then that wasn't surprising. Through the years I'd seen it happen again and again. I don't mean I knew exactly *how* it would happen, but lots of times, when they thought I was reading, or when I was playing over and over again one of the pieces I had memorized for a recital, I imagined it in a dozen different ways: a car accident, pneumonia, snakebite, drowning, food poisoning, lockjaw, cancer, tuberculosis, lightning, fire—I saw them all. It was amusing that among the possibilities I'd considered was the one it turned out to be. They'd always said I had a wonderful imagination—"too good" was the way they sometimes put it. Never for a moment did they have any idea how good it really was.

When I sat down in the wicker chair again, I decided to think about the funeral the next day. Aunt Helen was managing the whole thing. For years she directed the Little Theater plays—until the time Mrs. Goring butted in—and I think she got caught up in the funeral arrangements and saw it all like a production she had to bring off smoothly.

In all the imaginings I'd had I'd never imagined the funeral. I knew that if I thought about it ahead of time, it would help me act the way I wanted to. So I sat there, not seeing the cottonwood tree or the tea roses or the bright July sunlight. I watched myself at the funeral.

Sometimes when I think of how I felt that day in the back yard, and of how I feel now a year later, I wish that a limb from the cottonwood tree had crashed down on me and let me die happy.

Chapter 2

The first thing I saw the next morning was sunlight on the leaves of the elm tree outside my bedroom window. We were in the middle of a hot, dry spell, and rain hadn't seemed likely, but that was what I had wished for. Rain goes well at a funeral. It helps the funeral make you sad, and that's what funerals are for, to make you sad. And then, when they're over, and you've been to the cemetery, and all the relatives have gone home, you're free to start living without the person who died.

I lay in bed, looking at my gray dress hanging against the yellow wall, and tried to remember what I had dreamed. Usually I can remember my dreams. It helps not to move. If you lie still, keeping the same position in which you awake, the dream is more likely to come to you. On that morning I began to get a faint little feeling of the dream, just a glimmer, and then a thread, and I pulled, gently, gently, and the thread grew larger and stronger and the dream came out.

I was in a place of unearthly beauty, filled with grays and pale greens. There were very tall, giant trees all around, with luxurious growths of vines trailing down them. There was no land, only water, but that was all right, because I moved across the water with no difficulty, in fact, without even giving a thought to what I was doing. The water was clean and pure and beautiful.

Off to one side, far in the distance, I saw a small, dark figure, and something about it bothered me and was an intrusion on the peacefulness of the scene. But when I came closer, I saw it was only my old grandma, and I didn't need to worry about her. She was so nearsighted, she'd never recognize me and I wouldn't have to speak to her. I turned away, but just when I did her faint voice came across the water to me, calling my name over and over, "Dorrie, Dorrie."

I started running across the water away from her, and then suddenly everything was all right because I wasn't running any longer. I was on water skis and I could see my father in the boat ahead of me, his hands held over his head, giving me the high sign of encouragement.

I lay there for a while, thinking of the dream and of my beautiful, beautiful father. No one except me knew my father. What I'm saying could be misleading, but there is no other way to say it and it is true. If every single person in town had been asked, "Who is Dorrie Lawson's father?" all of them would have pointed to one man. And if I had been asked this question, I, too, would have pointed to this same man. But I was the only one who knew him. No one could really see him except me.

I decided to look through my poetry and I got up and took my hatbox down from the closet shelf. I looked through the poems and tried to pick out my favorite. My favorite changed from time to time. Just after I'd written one it would be my favorite for at least a week or two, but then gradually it wouldn't seem so good to me. On the day of the funeral the one I liked best was one I'd written a year before when my parents went to Las Vegas for a week. Most of my poems are written to my father and this one was too. I decided to memorize it. I would put it in my purse and from time to time during the funeral I would glance at it, and by the time the day was over, I'd have it in my mind. A good thing about memorizing that particular poem on that particular day was that it was a sad poem and it would help me be sad at the funeral. It was only four lines:

How foolish of you to go away from me,
Over there they won't know who you are.
And I, alone, in this strange city,
Don't know who I am.

I liked this poem especially well because of the phrase, "they won't know who you are." It wasn't just in Las Vegas that people didn't know who my father was. No one anywhere could appreciate him the way I could.

The poem was written on notebook paper and I decided to copy it on a stiff card. I put on my robe and went downstairs to my father's den. I found a card, and using my father's pen, I made a good, neat copy.

As I went back up the stairs, I could hear Mrs. Berkson moving around in her room. I had been very quiet, trying not to waken her. The longer she slept and the longer I had the house to myself, the better I liked it. In my room I slipped the card in my white purse and started getting dressed. I would have liked to put on shorts, but I was afraid they might look frivolous the day of a funeral, even in the early morning, so I put on a blouse and skirt.

The phone started ringing and I could hear Mrs. Berkson clopping down the stairs to answer it. I timed it just right, and when she lifted the receiver down there, I lifted the one in my room. I hadn't wanted a phone of my own, but they had decided it might make me more like other teen-agers. I put my hand over the mouthpiece and listened.

As I might have known, it was Aunt Helen, worrying about things. She didn't like the idea that I was going to be the only member of the immediate family at the funeral.

"Poor little girl," she was saying. "My heart goes out to her." Mrs. Berkson had never been known for her originality.

"Mine, too," she said. "She seems so lost. I hope she sleeps late this morning."

"Yes," my aunt answered, "let her sleep. It'll give her strength." The sigh she gave was long and drawn out.

She went on, "The hospital says there's absolutely no chance of release today. Maybe tomorrow, but the shock's been too much. Well, I'll be over around ten o'clock. Somehow we'll get her through this day. You know how we all appreciate your staying with her."

"Don't mention it," Mrs. Berkson was in her element. "I wouldn't of done anything else."

Mrs. Berkson was never happy unless she was doing something for someone. I'd watched her for years, ever since we'd moved across the alley from her. There was not the slightest sign that she knew how selfish her unselfishness really was. Somewhere along the line she'd swallowed the idea of the golden rule. What was so funny was that if someone asked her, "Who's the best woman in town?" and if she'd answered what she really thought, she would have said, "Why, I am, of course."

If my grandma hadn't been carrying on so, and if my aunt Helen could have stayed with me instead of her, Mrs. Berkson would have felt cheated.

They hung up, and so did I, and then I wandered downstairs and said hello to Mrs. Berkson and went on out in the back yard. The roses were fresh and beautiful in the morning sunlight, but I didn't really care for them. I went around to the north edge of our lawn to my own flower bed. Every year I grow marigolds. No flower can compare with them. They're brighter and more cheerful than anything you can grow. And nothing smells like a marigold. Their fragrance isn't sissy or sentimental. It's strong and pungent and dominates any other smell.

I went down the row of flowers, picking the ones that were in full bloom until finally I had a huge bouquet. From the cupboard on the back porch I got exactly the vase I wanted, short and purple and fluted. In the kitchen I ran water into it and then arranged the beautiful blossoms. The contrast of the yellows and golds was striking above the purple vase. I went upstairs to my parents' room and placed the vase on the bureau.

Because of my mother's hay fever, marigolds were never brought into the house. I lay down on her side of the bed and enjoyed the sight of them. I lay there a long time, enjoying the marigolds.

Finally Mrs. Berkson called up the stairs that breakfast was ready. She had made biscuits and cooked eggs and bacon. Ordinarily I wouldn't have wanted such a big breakfast, but that day it looked good to me. In spite of the fact that I ate well, she kept acting as though I weren't eating. Before I had a chance to sit down, she said, "Even though you don't feel like it, you really must eat. It'll help you hold up."

Through the rest of the day I stood off a way and watched myself do what was expected. That time they made me go see a psychologist, I told him that I sometimes did this. In his smart-aleck way he said, "You're more of a participating observer than an observing participator."

I almost laughed in his face. He was so in love with his own words. I knew he'd read them someplace.

I dressed the part that day of the funeral, wearing the costume Aunt Helen had chosen. And during the services at the church I memorized my poem. The few times I listened to the minister, it seemed as though he were talking about someone I'd never known. But I had expected that. At the cemetery I looked at the flowers, but they were too happy looking and I was afraid their happiness would show on my face, so I kept my eyes on the casket while the preacher mumbled his words.

He started on that business about "ashes to ashes, dust to dust" and Grandma gave a lurch. It was a good thing the minister from her church had his hand on her elbow. Grandma was looking smaller and older than I'd ever seen her—as though she might blow away in the hot July wind. Her minister bent his head down toward her, saying something, but I could tell by the way her wrinkled old face was drawn up, she was taking no comfort from him.

Grandma always did like to suffer. There was something in her that called for it. Hundreds of times when she had a headache, I've heard her say, "No, I've never been a hand for doping myself. I don't want any aspirin. I'll just wear it off."

But she didn't wear it off by herself. She made everyone help her, moping around and sighing and sniffing the camphor bottle. I found out all about that the summer they made me live with her.

And now her face showed plainly she was shutting out the minister's words. I wondered why the Bible wasn't a help to her. I remembered how she used to make me sit out on the back porch and learn parts of it, especially the Psalms, and in the Twenty-third, which she thought was so wonderful, was a place where it said, "Thy rod and thy staff they comfort me." She had read the Bible through eight and a half times and there were long parts of it she knew by heart, but from the way she had carried on ever since she heard about the accident, it wasn't doing her any good.

For three days everything had been leading up to the funeral and the burial, and finally it was over. Mrs. Berkson and my grandma and I rode back home in my aunt's car. I was hoping my aunt and my grandma would just let us out and go on, but they came in and stayed until after dark. Aunt Helen seemed a little let down; maybe she was sorry the show was over. She helped my grandma into the darkened living room and made her lie on the sofa. I went upstairs and changed my clothes and when I came down again, my aunt was sitting near my grandma in my father's chair. At first I thought they were talking, but when I listened, my grandma was saying over and over, "Jesus bless us. Jesus bless us."

When, finally, they went home, I felt that the day was behind me. I went to bed that night, looking forward to the next day and all the days to come.

Sometimes I wonder how I could have stopped what happened during this past year. Maybe if I had handled things differently, everything would be all right now. But then, again, it seems that what has happened was inevitable and that it started a long time ago. I don't know. I just don't know. I keep going back over my life and thinking about my mother and my father and the way things were for so long. But mostly I think about me.

Chapter 3

I woke up the next morning, not trying to remember my dreams, or with a poem coming to me line by line as though someone were dictating it, or filled with that terrible, familiar feeling that something bad was going to happen. I woke up in the bubble. I knew immediately what it was even though I'd never been in it before.

For a while I didn't move, but then I sat up slowly and slowly got out of bed and the bubble still surrounded me. I walked across the floor to my window and my movements were rounded and graceful and I knew that never again would anyone make remarks about my awkwardness.

My life was at its beginning. Gradually I would forget the old memories. I would get so used to being in the bubble that I'd forget there had ever been a time when I was outside it. I would forget the first time I'd ever seen it.

I must have been about four years old that day. My mother and father and I had gone to the beach at the lake. We walked along through the hot sand to find a spot near the edge of the water. I carried my bucket in one hand and my other hand was in my father's. Sand slid into my beach shoes and burned my feet, but that wasn't important. What was important was my father's hand holding mine. It connected us and made us a pair, and I don't think I even knew there was any difference in our heights. Where my mother walked, I don't remember. We came close to the edge of the lake. I wasn't used to the water then, and I thought how brave my father was to take us so near it. With him there I wasn't afraid. We settled down and I started working furiously, showing my father—without mentioning it to him—how hard I could work with my shovel and bucket. But my mother didn't want him to see. Right away she said, "For heaven's sake, Dorrie, you're spraying sand all over us. Go off a ways to do your digging."

I looked at my father, but he only said, "That's right, baby. Go over there to dig."

I went away from them. I went so far away that it was dangerous, and I thought my father would call me back to keep me safe and close. But he didn't. For a while I didn't look at them. I pretended everything was all right and that I was playing in the sand. I dug holes, filling my bucket with sand, but when it was full, I emptied it right back into the holes I had just dug. I didn't look at my parents.

But then I heard my mother say in her quiet voice, "Dorrie loves the beach. We must bring her more often."

I glanced at them then and saw that my mother was lying on her back and my father was lying close to her on his stomach, his arm across her shoulders. That was when I first saw the bubble. It was all around them, closing the two of them together, shutting me out. I forgot my shovel and pail and got up and ran and ran across the long space of sand and threw myself down on them.

My mother sat up, brushing sand off her. "What's the matter, Dorrie, are you hurt?" she asked.

My father put his arms around me and patted me, and when I could stop crying, I told them that I was afraid.

My father said, "Why, baby, there's nothing to be afraid of, you know that. It's broad daylight and Mommy and Daddy are right here."

I said, "I'm afraid of the water."

My mother said, "But you weren't even near the water."

She stood up then and held her hand out to me and said, "Come on with Mommy. Let's just get our feet wet a little. You'll see, it's fun."

But she didn't get me in the water, not that day or ever. And when finally I did get used to it, years later, it wasn't to please her.

And now, the day after the funeral, I was in the bubble myself. And when my father came home from the hospital that day, we'd be in it together. Dorrie Lawson and her father.

This was the day of my real birth. I looked at the calendar from Rourke's Hardware Store and drew a circle around the date. From that year on I'd have a secret birthday celebration on July 25.

As I dressed, the warm, safe feeling of the bubble stayed with me. Almost in a dream, I went downstairs. Mrs. Berkson was in the kitchen, putting the skillet on the stove.

"Hello, honey," she said. "How did you sleep?"

"I had a lovely sleep," I said.

She opened the refrigerator and started to take out the bacon.

"Mrs. Berkson," I said, "you've done so much. I know you must be wanting to get home. I'll fix my own breakfast."

She hesitated, and I could tell she really did want to leave. "I don't know, Dorrie," she said. "I told your aunt I'd stay until she got here."

"But you'll be so close," I said. "If anything comes up, I'll call you. I promise."

She set the bacon on the counter and started untying her apron strings. "All right, honey," she said. "But you be sure now, if you get to feeling blue or anything, you just give me a ring and I'll be right over."

"I'll be all right," I said. "You know my father's coming home today."

"I know," she said, and I thought she was going to start

crying, but she was satisfied with just letting her eyes mist up a little.

She got her night things and went out the back door. As I watched her cross the lawn I wished it were winter and I could build a fire in the fireplace and close the doors and shut out everyone except my father.

The phone started ringing and I was tempted not to answer it, but then I thought it might be the hospital calling. Instead it was Sandy Donovan. Sandy's the only person I know who doesn't make you lie to her. You'd think people would appreciate that when it's so rare. But they don't. Time and again my mother had said, "I don't know what you see in her."

And once, when I was listening outside my parents' bedroom door, I heard her say to my father, "Out of all the girls in this town, why she has to choose that one for a friend, I don't understand."

"I know," my father answered. "Why, that kid isn't even bright. With Dorrie's intelligence, I don't see how she puts up with her."

"It's beyond me," my mother said. "Heaven knows I've tried. I wanted to have a Valentine party for her this year, but no, she's not the least bit interested. And if you try to go ahead and do something anyway, it's like running through water, she makes it so hard."

When I heard Sandy's voice on the phone, I relaxed and told her the truth. "No, I'd rather you didn't come over," I said. "I just want to think about my father coming home."

I hung up and went out to the kitchen and put the bacon and the skillet away and got myself a piece of cheddar cheese out of the refrigerator. I had known a long time that cheese is very nutritious. There's no reason to eat bacon and eggs every day of your life.

When I had eaten, I went into the living room and started rearranging the furniture. Many times I'd dreamed of this. I took all of the books out of the bookcase and moved it over against the south wall. When I replaced them, I did it by subject matter instead of by size and color. It made much better sense.

Then I pulled the sofa out of the middle of the room and pushed it under the front windows. In winter I would move it back in front of the fireplace, but for summer it would be nice to have the light from the windows at your back when you wanted to read.

I put the Morris chairs on either side of the fireplace—one for my father and one for me. On one side of his I put the little end table that had always been in the spare room at the head of the stairs.

I took everything off the mantel—the half-dead ivy in its pink elephant planter, the brass candleholders my mother had won as a door prize, her bowling trophy, and the picture of my mother and my aunt as little girls. I put it all in the cupboard on the back porch.

I liked the gate-legged table against the east wall. I opened one end and put a green linen cloth over it. Then I went outside and picked a small bouquet of marigolds and put them in the center of the table.

I was just starting to dust when my aunt came.

"Hello, Dorrie, darling," she said, and I could tell she had decided that a shade more cheerful tone of voice was all right for the day.

She saw the dustcloth. "What a good girl you are," she said. "You'll be such a comfort to Jim."

She looked around then, and the wrinkles came into her forehead, and in a worried way she said, "You've moved the furniture."

I'd learned to outwit her long ago.

"Yes," I said, "I thought it might help."

"Yes, yes . . . I suppose you may be right," she said. Then

she decided for sure. "You are right. It will help your father. How thoughtful of you, Dorrie."

She went out to the kitchen and I heard her open the refrigerator door. When she came back she said, "Well, you've certainly got plenty of food in the house. People have been so good. Did you eat breakfast, darling?"

I told her I had and she looked at me admiringly and said, "You're being such a big girl. Your mother would be so proud of you."

She went upstairs then to collect the laundry. I knew that later there would be a showdown and I'd make her understand that I was going to wash our clothes myself. But I thought that for this once I would let her do it.

When she came downstairs, it wasn't the laundry she was carrying. She had my card in her hand, my card with my poem on it.

"Oh, Dorrie," she said, with tears spilling out of her eyes, "this just breaks my heart, it's so beautiful. It's the loveliest tribute your mother could have."

She didn't notice the coldness of my voice. "What were you doing in my purse?" I asked her.

"Looking for your handkerchiefs, darling," she answered.

She sat on the sofa and reread my poem, and I wanted to snatch it out of her hand and yell, "But, you fool, it's written for my father, do you understand?"

Her face twisted up and for the first time I saw her actually cry. It wasn't at all becoming. She was too old. I could see how ugly she was going to be when those lines and wrinkles were there permanently. You would never have known she and my mother had been sisters. Crying only made my mother better looking.

I wanted to get rid of her, with her tears and her carrying on. I said, "Aunt, could I confide something in you?"

She loved it. "Of course you can, darling. You can tell me anything, anytime. You know that."

"Well," I said, and I paused a little as though it were hard to go on, "there's one thing that always makes me feel better if I'm sad."

"Yes, Dorrie?" She was ready to move heaven and earth to make me feel better.

"Well, it may seem funny to you," I continued, "but if I can be alone to write out my thoughts, it makes me feel better than anything can."

There was an instant's pause. Just letting me alone and leaving the house wasn't what she'd had in mind. She glanced at the poem, blinked her eyes, and said, "I see what you mean, honey. I can understand what a relief it would be to be able to put down your thoughts so beautifully. I have a little of the artist in me, too, you know."

She took the laundry and left soon after that, and I put my poem back in the hatbox. Later I was going to find a place in one of my drawers for my poetry. I wouldn't need to keep it hidden from my mother any longer.

Several people called up that morning and wanted to help me, but I said the right things and kept them from coming to the house.

When lunch time came, I looked in the refrigerator. It was jammed with casseroles and jello salads and cakes and pies. Even with all the people eating there the last few days, they'd hardly made a dent in the food which had been given us. None of it looked good to me, and I opened a can of corn and heated it with a lot of butter and salt and pepper and ate all of it.

When I had finished eating, I went upstairs to my parents' bedroom. I took off all my clothes and looked at myself in the full-length mirror on the back of the door. People had complimented my mother on her figure, but mine was better. She never dressed without putting on a girdle; I didn't even own one. I turned this way and that, glad that I wasn't one of those flat-chested girls who develop late.

I went into the bathroom and sat in the tub and rubbed soap and water on my legs until I had a good lather. Then, with my mother's razor, I carefully shaved, first my legs, then my underarms. When I had finished, I ran water in the tub, hot and fast, and directly under the stream of it I poured my mother's bath salts. A sweet lilac fragrance filled the room. When the tub was almost full, I turned the water off and lay back, relaxing for a long time.

When finally I got out and dried myself, I felt of my legs. They were smooth and soft, but I took my mother's hand lotion and rubbed it over every inch of my body.

Then I lay naked on my parents' bed. The marigolds I'd put on the bureau the day before were still bright and beautiful. Their fragrance mixed with the fragrance of the bath salts but was stronger.

My parents' bedroom was the biggest, best room in the house, as large as the dining room and the sunporch, which were below, combined. It was decorated in my mother's favorite colors—pink and white and blue. The bedspread I lay on was satin and pink and soft, and I was probably the first person who had ever lain on the bed without turning it back.

Pink and white and blue are colors for a young girl's room, and when they redecorated my room, that was what I'd wanted. But my mother settled that argument fast. She said, "Your room is on the north, Dorrie, and calls for brightness. Yellow would be perfect in it." So I not only had a bedroom on the coldest and darkest side of the house, but a color not of my own choosing. But as I lay on my parents' bed that day, I knew that this was only one of many things that were never going to bother me again.

Later I got up to get dressed for my father. But first I took my parents' wedding picture from the bureau. I stood looking at it. My father had always been handsome. I put the picture face down under my mother's clothes in the bottom drawer of the bureau and went into my room. I put on my best bra and panties and my prettiest slip. Then I put on my pink sheath, which was the most sophisticated thing my mother had ever let me buy, and with it my pink heels.

My mother's hairbrush was better than mine and I sat at her dresser, brushing my hair over and over again. Then I fooled around until I learned how to sweep it up into a French roll in back. I put on my mother's chalk-white earrings and beads, outlined my mouth with her pearl-pink lipstick, and touched her Tabu perfume to my ears, and loved the way I looked and felt.

For years I'd wanted to have Tabu perfume, but my mother always said, "Dorrie, it just isn't the proper thing for a young girl. A lighter, flower scent is more appropriate. Just wait, honey, you'll grow up fast enough and then Mommy will see to it that you have Tabu if that's what you still want."

I was standing in front of the full-length mirror again when the doorbell rang. Slowly and gracefully I walked down the stairs.

A young man stood at the door. "Hello," he said, "is the lady of the house in?"

I stood tall and straight. I smelled the fragrance of the Tabu perfume. I smiled at him and said, "I'm the lady of the house."

He was selling a set of books designed for children. I told him we had no children but that the Wilsons, three doors down, did. I liked the way he tipped his hat before he turned to go.

I was still standing at the door when the evening paper came sailing into the yard. I brought it in and opened it and smoothed it out. Then I folded it once and lay it on the end table by my father's Morris chair. I took a cigar from the humidor and put it with matches in a big ash tray beside the paper.

I went to the kitchen and set a tray on the counter. On it I put the scotch, a coaster, and a stirrer. I took a glass from the cupboard and ran hot water in it and polished it until it shone. Then I took ice cubes from the refrigerator and put some of them in the ice pail. I looked at the tray to see if I'd forgotten anything and I remembered the jigger and water. Finally I took the tray into the living room and set it on the coffee table between our chairs.

I was just going to put water on to boil, in case he might want coffee instead, when I glanced out the living room window, and there, coming up the walk, was my father.

Chapter 4

✀ ✀ ✀ ✀ ✀ ✀ ✀ ✀ ✀ ✀ ✀ ✀
✀ ✀ ✀ ✀ ✀

I flew out the front door and into my father's arms.

"Daddy, Daddy," I cried. I hugged him tight and felt I'd never let him go.

He said, "There, there, now, baby," and gently freed himself.

I put my arm through his and we walked in step, exactly in step, up the front sidewalk to the house. I could feel the bubble all around us.

He went straight to his chair in the living room, and there he was, with his cigar on his right and his scotch in front of him and me opposite him. Everything was perfect.

"You look thin, Daddy," I said.

"Yes, yes, I suppose." He rubbed his hand over his eyes. "It's been hard," he said.

"I know," I said. "Being in the hospital isn't any fun."

For a moment he didn't answer. He sighed and put his head back against the chair with his eyes closed. Then he said, "I wish I could have been with you, Dorrie. I just couldn't do it. I'm sorry I let you down."

"You've never let me down, Daddy," I cried. "You never could."

He still had his eyes closed, so I said, "Do you want a drink? A scotch and water? I'll fix it for you." He opened his eyes and noticed the tray in front of him.

"No, no, thanks, baby, I don't think so," he said.

"Coffee? I'll fix you some coffee."

"No, nothing now." He closed his eyes again. "I don't want anything now," he said.

I knew then that he just wanted to sit there and rest and enjoy being home with me. I knew how to be quiet. For half an hour I didn't say a thing. I just sat still and looked at him.

My father is tall and thick and strong, but he's not as tall as I used to think he was. One Christmas before I started to school, I was out in the back yard with Johnny Blake and Geraldine Wright and we were telling about our Christmas trees. I said, "Ours comes up and touches the ceiling. It's the same size as my daddy."

Johnny said, "You're a liar. Your daddy doesn't either touch the ceiling. Nobody's daddy does."

I stamped my foot and said, "You just come in right now and I'll show you, so there."

When we were in the house, I saw there really was a space between my father's head and the ceiling. After that I knew he wasn't as tall as I had thought; he was only taller than other men.

The phone rang and Daddy opened his eyes, but I jumped up and went in the den to answer it. It was Virginia Stevenson. She and my mother had been best friends and the Stevensons had been in and out of our house ever since the accident.

"Hello, Dorrie," she said. "Has your father come home yet?"

"Yes," I said, "he's resting. He's terribly tired."

"I know he must be," she said, "the poor darling. Well, listen, Dan and I thought maybe a little later this evening we'd drop by for a while."

I said, "I don't know, Virginia. Being in the hospital has been awfully hard on him."

She said, "We wouldn't stay long. I think it might do him good. You know, honey, we've been friends a long time now."

I lowered my voice. "To tell you the truth," I said, "he hopes we'll be let alone tonight. He said so."

"Oh, well, that's different," she said. If she was hurt, she kept it from showing in her voice. "Tell him I called, and we're thinking of you both and we'll be over some time soon."

I went back to the living room and told my father it had been Virginia calling. I said, "She says they'll be over some time soon."

"All right," he said. His tone was listless. He sounded as though he didn't care whether he ever saw the Stevensons again, and I was glad. We didn't need them.

I said, "Don't worry, Daddy. We don't have to be bothered with them. We can discourage them."

"What do you mean, baby?" he asked.

I said, "Well, just gradually we'll let them know they aren't welcome any more. And we won't go to see them."

"We can't do that, honey," he said. "You're upset right now. You'll feel differently later. We can't hurt their feelings."

I saw then how it might be, how it could be. I saw the way my father was seeing it. He and I and the Stevensons would be a foursome.

I said, "You're right, Daddy. We can't hurt their feelings."

As it turned out, I didn't get to do as much for my father that evening as I had planned to. He never did smoke his cigar or want any scotch or coffee. He didn't even eat. He didn't notice how nice the living room looked.

It grew dark and I went around turning on the lights. At nine o'clock I tuned the radio to the FM program he always liked, but when the music came into the living room, he got up and went upstairs.

He came down almost immediately and looked directly at me and said, "Where's the wedding picture?"

"It's in a bureau drawer," I said. "I'll get it."

He followed me up the stairs and took the picture from my hand and sat down on his bed staring at it. I began to have a strange feeling, awkward and uncomfortable. Then I got the idea that he didn't want me in the bedroom with him. No, not that. He didn't know I was in the bedroom with him.

Slowly I went out and across the hall to my own room and closed the door. I lay down on my bed and pulled my Teddy bear over to me and rubbed his ear.

I tried to be happy about the next day. I tried to think of how it was going to be having my father to myself. But something kept coming back into my mind. When Daddy had come down the stairs and asked me about the wedding picture, it was the first time he'd looked at me since he came home. Before that he hadn't been seeing me. I wasn't there for him. She was still there. I wasn't in the bubble.

I grabbed my Teddy bear by the neck and threw him across the room. I turned on my stomach and doubled my fists and pounded the bed. And then I cried.

But I'm no crybaby. I never have been. I put a quick end to the tears. I went into the bathroom and washed my face. Then I went to the door of my father's room and called good night to him.

I tiptoed downstairs and dialed Sandy's number. I let the phone ring once and hung up. I slipped out the back door and took my sandals from the cupboard on the porch and put them on. Then I went down the alley to the park. When I climbed under the bridge, Sandy was there waiting.

The one ring had meant emergency, and now she said, "What's up?"

"Everything," I said. "He's still thinking of her. He doesn't even see me. He doesn't know I'm around."

"How can you tell?" she asked.

"I just can," I said. I never bothered trying to explain things to Sandy.

She pushed her hair back out of her eyes. "What are you going to do?" she asked.

"I don't know. I just don't know. I've got to figure something out."

She didn't say anything for a minute and neither did I, but then she let out a groan and said, "Oh, God, I hate her."

I said, "I do too. I hate her too."

I felt so sad right then I could have started crying all over again. I was reminded of all the times I'd told Sandy how I hated my mother and of all the times she'd said she hated her too.

And here we were, with my mother finally dead, sitting under the bridge, still saying it.

I picked up a rock and slammed it down into Jersey Creek. Just at the moment it hit the water, the nine-o'clock train whistled down at Greeley's crossing. It gave me the feeling that my throwing the rock had made the train whistle. I wasn't sure it hadn't. For a long time I'd noticed that cause and effect wasn't the simple thing people thought. I hadn't figured out the real system, but for years I'd been trying to. I knew there was a pattern somewhere, a system that made sense on some level. One thing I knew for sure was that imagining things was far more important than most people knew. There were ways to make things happen without even raising your little finger.

"God damn it," Sandy said, and then she started crying.

I patted her shoulder and said, "It's all right. Everything will work out all right," but I didn't really try to get her to stop crying. When she cried, I didn't have to.

Finally her crying turned into sniffling and gradually that, too, stopped. She reached in her pocket and said, "Want a cigar?"

I'd taught her that smoking cigarettes was out of date, everyone did it. I took the cigar and peeled it and crumpled the wrapper in my hand and threw it down toward the creek. Seeing the glisten of one of the park lights on the water made me think of how my mother had died. But I knew it wasn't my fault. No one could blame me. I couldn't help it if I had a headache that day.

Sandy handed me the matches, and as I struck one I thought that sooner or later all the kids would take up smoking cigars and cigar smoking would be ruined too.

Sandy giggled. "The last time I smoked a cigar my grandmother thought there was a man in the house," she said.

"That's a good one," I said. It was, too. Sandy's grandmother was old and stone deaf except for her hearing aid and just about blind as well. No man would be interested in her. And Sandy, well, Sandy wasn't likely to attract a man to the house. Even though she was my only friend, I wasn't blind to her looks. She had the kind of oily skin that was broken out most of the time and her hair was a greasy, nothing color.

The first time my parents saw Sandy was just after she moved to town. She and I weren't friends yet. Somehow she found out where I lived and one night she came to the door and asked for me. My father invited her into the living room. He came out to the kitchen where my mother and I were doing dishes and said, "There's a girl here to see you, Dorrie."

My mother brightened. "You go right along, honey," she said. "I'll finish in here."

I couldn't imagine what girl would be coming to see me. I went into the living room and it was the new girl, standing awkwardly, her weight on one foot, a streak of mud up the side of her leg, looking uncomfortable and out of place in our softly lighted house.

"Hi, Dorrie," she said. "I wonder if you could give me the English assignment."

I knew immediately that she was lying—she didn't give two hoots about the English assignment. She had been in class only a few days but long enough for me and everyone else to know she didn't bother doing homework.

But something kept me from laughing at her. She knew so well how out of place she was. She knew so well that even if I gave her the assignment, and even if she studied it, she wouldn't be able to learn it. But more than anything else, I could see exactly how she would look to my mother.

I said, "Sure, Sandy, I'll get it for you. Sit down. I'll go up to my room and write it out."

When I came back downstairs, my mother, with her usual eagerness, had opened a couple of cokes and poured them into glasses and was standing in the living room. The expression on her face was priceless. She'd just taken a good look at Sandy and she wasn't at all the little friend my mother had been dreaming of finding for me.

I introduced them, and then I said, "Sandy, I've been wishing you'd come to see me ever since you moved to town."

Sandy looked as though she couldn't quite believe such good news but she was going to be happy about it anyway. She smiled and said, "Me, too."

I said, "Come on upstairs. I want to show you my room."

We went up and I closed the door and turned on my radio so no one could hear us talk. That very first night I found out what a wonderful friend Sandy could be. I kept her there for two hours until, finally, my mother knocked on the door and said, "Bedtime, Dorrie."

When Sandy had gone, my father said, "Who on earth was that?"

My mother said, "Really, Dorrie, she looks like something the cat dragged in."

"It just happens," I said, "that Sandy Donovan's my best friend." At the moment I said it, I knew it was true.

My cigar kept going out and finally I handed it to Sandy and told her to keep it until next time. She slipped it into her pocket and I stood up and brushed off the back of my pink sheath. Sandy also stood up and brushed off the back of her skirt.

"Well, I'll see you," I said.

"See you," she answered, and she started off to the west and I to the east.

When I got home, the door to my father's room was open and the room was empty. I went through the whole house and out into the yard and around the house, but he was gone. He hadn't left a note for me; he'd thought I was in bed, asleep. I knew where he was. He was at the cemetery with her.

I went back into the empty house and up to my room, feeling as lost and alone as I ever had. I glanced at the calendar with the red ring around the date where that morning I had marked the beginning of my life in the bubble. I undressed and noticed there were grass stains on my pink sheath, but I didn't care. I didn't brush my teeth or wash my face, and long ago I'd gotten over saying my prayers. I turned out the duck lamp and crawled into bed and all around me was the blackness and the blankness. It was familiar to me, but now worse than ever, because for a short while that day I'd felt in the bubble.

At last I heard my father come home and go into his room. Just having him in the house made me feel a little better. I got up and washed my face and hands and brushed my teeth. This time, just before I turned out the duck lamp, I took my red pencil and blanked out the date, July 25, filling in completely the circle I'd made that morning.

Now that my mother was dead and my father was home with me, things weren't the way I'd always thought they'd be. But I wasn't giving up. I climbed into bed promising myself that some day I'd draw a red circle around a date, and it would be the real date next time, the real date when I started living in the bubble with my father.

Chapter 5

❧ ❧ ❧ ❧ ❧ ❧ ❧ ❧ ❧ ❧ ❧ ❧ ❧ ❧

That night I dreamed that my mother and father and I were back in the little house on Maple Street where I'd spent the first years of my life. When I woke up that morning, there was no need to try to remember my dream. It was one of the strong ones that you see all over again, with your eyes wide open, without even trying to.

It was raining in my dream, the dark, gloomy rain I'd wanted for the funeral. My father was in the back yard with a gunny sack gathering walnuts. He didn't seem to notice he was getting wet, and I knocked on the kitchen window and motioned for him to come in. My mother was standing at the kitchen stove, stirring something, and she said, "Don't pester Daddy." She untied her apron strings and went out of the room. My father came through the kitchen door, carrying the gunny sack on his back. He went down into the basement and started looking for my mother. He couldn't find her and I was afraid he'd blame me.

With the dream still strong in me, I could see the house on Maple Street, room by room, the way it had been years before. I reminded myself that all of that was in the past.

I got up and went across the hall and quietly opened the door of my father's room. He was sound asleep, sprawled out in the middle of the bed. The sun was already in the room, and I went to the window and gently pulled the shade. As I was leaving, I noticed the wedding picture back in its place on the bureau. I pulled the door closed and put on my robe and went downstairs. In the kitchen I set water on to boil and made a pot of drip coffee and took a cup of it to the back porch.

Mrs. Berkson was already out, hanging up clothes, and I moved a little to one side so the cottonwood tree hid me from her. Someone up the street was cutting grass, and occasionally a car went by, but there was a quietness in our yard. I looked at the tea roses and the sun dancing on the cottonwood leaves and the glisten of dew on the grass. The coffee I sipped was good, and my father was upstairs in bed. I told myself that everything was fine, but the dream held part of me back to the days when we lived in the house on Maple Street.

After we moved away from there, I never again heard my parents making love, but the arrangement of the two small bedrooms in the little house was such that I could almost hear them breathe. The knowledge of their love-making was a part of me for as long as I can remember anything. I've no idea when I first heard them.

I didn't understand what was going on at first. I thought my father was hurting my mother. I sat at the breakfast table one morning, looking at my father's hands and saying to myself, "These are the hands that hurt my mother." As I grew a little older, my ideas about it changed and I began to realize that my mother loved the whole business. Then I began wanting to be in on it some way myself. I lay there listening to them, not wanting to be left out.

One night, in the middle of their love-making, I got up and went to the bathroom. When they came in to see what was keeping me there so long, I pretended I was sick and was going to vomit. Ordinarily that would have held their attention. But that night they soon grew tired of waiting and we all went back to bed. My interrupting them hadn't done any good at all. They went right on with their love-making, forgetting all about me.

As well as I could hear my parents, and as much as I tried to figure out exactly what was going on, I didn't really know until years later in third grade when Barbara Jenkins told me about Father's uncle's Cousin Kate. Before that I had never connected the word I saw scrawled in filling-station toilets with what my parents did at night. I don't mean I didn't know anything at all. But I had some crazy ideas.

I was out in Blake's garage one day with Johnny when he pulled down his pants and pointed his penis up and shot a stream of urine high in the air. I could see he had only one penis. But I had listened to my father urinate. He would go a little and then stop and then start again. I thought he had several penises and the fact didn't seem at all surprising.

The sun didn't shine much during those years on Maple Street. In summer there were many dark, rainy days. During the nights there would be great storms, with lightning and thunder and sudden bursts of rain. The lights would be out and my father would light a kerosene lamp and my mother would get me out of bed and put my shoes on me in case one of the giant elms crashed down on the house and we had to run out. In winter, too, the days were dark and bleak, filled with wind and cold and snow.

The house itself was a dark, damp little house. It had pulled away from its foundation, and in our living room there was a wide crack between the front door and the floor. When the light was on in the basement, it was especially noticeable and I worried for fear the house would fall down.

On nights when my parents didn't make love I would lie in bed, tense, ready to jump out if the walls started giving way. I planned to roll under the bed where I might be safe, but then I worried for fear the floor would fall into the basement and I'd be pinned down there in the water that was always on the floor after a day or two of rain. Or if there had been no rain, the big black water bugs would be there, running over me while I lay helpless.

Sometimes during these years the sun shone. But almost never when we were at home. There were sunny days at my grandma's house across town. There was sunshine at the beach. Sometimes there was sunshine at church.

Miss Blake, my Sunday-school teacher, lived across the street from us, and it was raining, raining, a heavy, steady, black downpour, one Saturday afternoon when she backed her car out of the garage and swung it around to our side of the street to pick me up to take me to the first rehearsal of the Christmas program.

When we got to the church, no one else had shown up. We waited around for a while, and then we ran out to the car to go home. On the way she stopped at the drugstore and when we went inside, she didn't ask me what I wanted. She just ordered two chocolate sundaes. It was the first sundae I'd ever had, and I thought that Sunday-school teachers ate sundaes, and I thought Miss Blake was wonderful.

When we got back to our street, Miss Blake came into my house with me. My mother had gone someplace and my father was in the kitchen under the sink, trying to fix a stopped up drain. He washed his hands and made some coffee and they sat at the table drinking it. There seemed to be something funny, and they laughed a lot and I wanted to laugh with them, but I couldn't tell when they were going to, so I just sat in my cut-down high chair with my Teddy bear on my lap and smiled.

After a while Miss Blake asked Daddy if he would help with the Christmas program. He said he would, and as she got up to leave, she said, "All right, Jim, you'll be stage manager, in charge of properties. Who knows, maybe this production will go on to Broadway."

They laughed some more, and when she had gone I kept saying to myself, "Stage manager." My father was going to be stage manager. Dorrie Lawson's father was going to be stage manager and Dorrie Lawson was going to be an angel. My mother wasn't going to be anything.

At the next rehearsal my father and I walked together to the church. I had never been so important in my whole life. We stopped for a traffic light on Chestnut Street, and Johnny Blake came along carrying a loaf of bread and I could see how it looked to Johnny. Mr. Lawson, the stage manager, was walking down the street with his daughter, an angel. They belonged together. You could tell that by the way he took her hand when they crossed the street.

I wanted to say something, just anything, to my father. I wanted us to be walking along, talking together. But I was too excited to think of anything to say. Some of the kids were jumping around outside the church building and I wondered if they saw Dorrie Lawson and her father coming.

Inside the church everything was warm and golden. Miss Blake was at the piano, playing "Away in a Manger," and Bobby Rollins was in the middle aisle, putting on his bathrobe, getting ready to be one of the three wise men, even though he wasn't supposed to wear his costume for this first practice.

I pulled Daddy over to the piano, and Miss Blake finished the ending of the song and turned and smiled at me. Then she looked at Daddy and put one hand to the back of her yellow hair and pushed up on it a little and said, "Hi. I'm glad you could come." She looked happy to have us there, and her face got a little pink and she fooled around with her beads. I was glad that Miss Blake and Daddy and I were being happy together.

All of the rehearsals were happy. Lots of funny things happened. I didn't exactly know what they were, but that didn't make any difference. It made me feel good to hear Daddy and Miss Blake laughing so much.

On the last practice night it was raining hard, and it rained on the manger Daddy had made. He put it in the back of our car and said it wouldn't hurt it to get wet; it wasn't supposed to be very fancy anyway. At the church I held open the door, and Daddy carried the manger in and up to the platform.

That night it was while Daddy and Miss Blake were fixing the manger that the laughing started. She was leaning over putting straw in it, and Daddy was on one side and I was on the other, and he reached over to unbutton my raincoat and a button on his coat caught in Miss Blake's hair. He pulled back and Miss Blake let out a little yell, but it didn't hurt her, because all the time Daddy was getting her loose, she kept laughing.

Daddy went down into the basement and got a stepladder and put it on the stage for the angels. When Miss Blake rapped on the pulpit and said it was time for everyone to get on the stage, Daddy picked me up and set me on the very top of the ladder. I would be the highest angel and the spotlight would be on me when I said my piece.

The night of the program, when the curtains parted, I was sitting nice and straight on top of the stepladder, feeling as though I really were an angel. Bobby Rollins came on the stage with his gift for the baby Jesus and tripped on the sash of his robe and almost fell down, but everything else went the way we had practiced it. When it was just about time for me to say my piece, I twisted around and looked behind the scenery so I could see Daddy watching me, being proud.

But when I looked, everything was all wrong. It was like a love movie back there. Miss Blake was kissing Daddy. The spotlight came on me and I was supposed to talk, but the words that I had known so well were gone and I just sat there. Then Daddy was wiping his mouth with his handkerchief, and he looked up at me as though he were surprised to see me. He tried to smile, but it was hard for him.

From then on I hated Miss Blake for what she had done to my father, making it hard for him to smile when before he had been so happy. I stopped being good in Sunday-school and I never was in another Christmas program.

My mother would say, "But, honey, just because you forgot your piece once doesn't mean you will again. Why, you're wonderful at memorizing." But I'd had enough of Christmas programs and Sunday-school teachers.

As I grew older, I realized even more how scheming Miss Blake had been. She'd been after my father from the beginning. Sometimes I thought maybe I shouldn't blame her. Living across the street from him, where she saw him often, and always being on the outside, must have been hard. But I did blame her. He was my father and no one had a right to kiss him.

Now Mrs. Berkson had worked her way down to the end of her clothesline, and before I could move out of her line of vision, she saw me and waved and called, "Hi, Dorrie. How are you this morning?"

"Fine," I called back, and stood up and went toward the kitchen door so she wouldn't try to keep me there talking. I knew that for years to come she would expect me to thank her for staying with me when my mother died. And she'd be going around saying, "It wasn't that I did so much, not anything anyone wouldn't of done. But the poor child was so grateful."

One of her favorite phrases was, "I like people," accenting the *like* and *people*. I had never understood why it was such a virtue to go around liking people indiscriminately, and it certainly was no compliment to be liked by someone who liked everyone. But really, what she was saying when she said this was how good she was. Almost all of her actions and words were designed to make people say, "She's a *good* woman."

I went into the kitchen and I could hear Daddy moving around in his room. I poured a cup of coffee and was just starting up the stairs with it when the phone rang. It was Virginia Stevenson, inviting us to dinner that night. Again I saw the foursome we would make.

"Why, I'd love to," I said, "but let me ask Daddy."

He said, "I suppose so, Dorrie. It doesn't matter. Whatever you want."

I went to the phone in my room. "We'll be there," I said, and I made no effort to keep the cheerfulness out of my voice. The funeral was over.

"Between six-thirty and seven then," she said and hung up.

Even though Daddy had slept late, he looked terrible, with dark shadows under his eyes and lines in his face that had never been there before. I wanted to cook bacon and eggs for him, but all he would eat was a little cold cereal and a piece of toast. I sat across the table from him, remembering how it had grown to be a joke between him and my mother that in the mornings he was bright and talkative and she was quiet and wanted to be left alone.

"It's going to be another hot day," I said. He looked out the window at the sunny morning.

I sipped my coffee and waited a few minutes and then I said, "Before we know it, summer will be over."

"Yes," he said absently.

I knew that what I had said was terribly uninteresting and I tried to think of something better, but the more I tried, the blanker I became. And then, because we usually went to the lake a couple of times in August, and August was almost there, I said, "When are we going to the lake, Daddy?"

He put down his coffee cup and slammed his fist down on

the table, and through clenched teeth, and looking straight at me, he said, "I never want to see that lake again. *Have you no feeling?*"

He got up from the table and went through the hall to the living room. I sat there, shocked and numb, feeling as though he'd slapped me. I knew I shouldn't have mentioned the lake. It was just that I'd been so desperate to think of something to say so we could have a breakfast conversation. I hadn't wanted to make a terrible mistake like that. I'd wanted to be good.

For the second time since my father had come home from the hospital I knew I was going to cry. Nobody ever sees me cry, and I had to get safely to my room first. I got up and headed for the stairs. My father came out of the living room and called my name.

I turned and he came to me and put his hands on my shoulders. "I'm sorry, baby," he said. "I didn't mean that. I forget how young you are."

His hands on me were wonderful and I felt safe and warm. I could have cried then for happiness.

"It's all right, Daddy," I said. "Everything's going to be all right."

Chapter 6

≥≥≥≥≥≥≥≥≥≥≥≥≥≥≥≥≥≥≥≥

Later that morning my aunt came over. I was in the kitchen, scraping all the food that had been given to us into the garbage disposal. Her shrill voice cut through the air like a knife.

"Jim, Jim, dear, where are you?" she was calling before she was even halfway in the house.

"In here, Helen," my father answered, and she went into the living room with him.

I went into the hall and listened long enough to know what they were talking about. She was offering to take care of sending cards to everyone who had sent flowers and done things for us. That was fine with me. I went back to my work in the kitchen and I had just finished putting the last of the dirty dishes in the dishwasher when she and my father came in.

"Hello, darling," my aunt said. "How are you this morning? Is there any coffee left?"

I poured three cups and took the sugar out of the cupboard for my aunt and we sat at the kitchen table. Then she started.

"Now, Jim," she said, "I've been doing some thinking."

For a moment she didn't go on. She took a sip of her coffee and looked out the window. We were supposed to sit there, hanging on to her every word. I didn't play her game. I started into the hall.

But this wasn't the way she'd planned the scene.

"Come back, Dorrie," she said. "This concerns you too."

I took my time sitting down again, first going to the sink and getting a glass of water.

Again she sipped her coffee. "As I said, I've been doing some thinking. We've got to get things organized here before school starts."

"Organized?" my father asked, and it was as though he spoke for me.

"Yes," my aunt said. "School is not much more than a month away. I'll do what I can, but with Mother not well, I can't do a lot. What you need is someone here to look after you. We've got to find a good housekeeper."

Before, she had only irritated me. Now I felt the anger rise in me and I said, "Aunt, I'm going to keep house for us. We don't want anyone else here."

My voice had been louder than usual and now she lowered hers. She reached across the table and patted my hand. "I know how you feel, darling," she said. "You don't want someone coming in, trying to take your mother's place. Believe me, no one will try to do that."

"Aunt," I said, "please just let us alone. We're going to get along fine. I've got it all figured out."

"I know you would do your best," she said, "and don't think I don't admire your spirit. But the responsibility of the cooking and cleaning and going to school would be too much for any girl your age."

I said, "Daddy, don't let her do this. Don't let her do this to us."

Before he could answer, my aunt said to him, "I've been asking around. I've heard of a couple of women who might do. Shall I go ahead and find someone?"

For a moment my father hesitated.

"It's for the best, Jim," my aunt said. "Believe me, you need someone,"

"All right, Helen," he said then. "Go ahead. I guess it's a good idea."

"And one more thing," she went on. "Someone's got to go through Eleanore's things and decide what to do with them."

I thought immediately of the dressing-table drawer which my mother had always kept locked. I'd planned to go through all her other drawers, looking for the key, as soon as my father started going back to work and I had time.

My father got up from the table and went to the back door, and I wondered if he were just going to walk away without answering my aunt. He stood there with his back to us.

"I know it's painful, Jim," Aunt Helen said, "but the sooner it's faced, the better. I can come over and do it if you like."

"Can't it wait a while?" my father asked.

"The sooner, the better," my aunt repeated.

For a long time I'd wanted to know what secret my mother kept locked in that lower left-hand drawer. My aunt wasn't going to take my chance away from me.

"Daddy," I said, "why should we rush into getting rid of my mother's things? What's the hurry? Can't we decide anything for ourselves?"

"Dorrie's right." My father turned and faced my aunt. "I know you mean well, Helen, but there's no hurry. Sometime later."

My father went up to his room and my aunt poured herself another cup of coffee.

"How did you come out on your writing yesterday?" she asked me.

For a moment I didn't know what she was talking about, but then I remembered. "Oh, all right," I said.

"Anything I can see?" she wanted to know.

"Well, no, Aunt," I said, "not anything that's really finished."

She gave me a smile and said, "You just keep at it, darling."

I began to wonder if it would be a good idea to take my poetry from the hatbox and put it in one of my drawers. She was awfully interested in it, and after all, she was my mother's sister. She'd probably snoop too.

Before she left that morning, I went with her to her car and helped her bring in our laundry which she had already washed and ironed. I smiled when I saw my father's shirts, hanging on hangers, starched as stiff as Aunt Helen's own lacquered hair. He'd never wear them like that. I'd have to do them over.

She tried to get me to go to my grandma's with her, but I told her I had a headache and at last she drove away and left us in peace.

When I went in to clean the living room, I saw that my father had had a drink that morning. He never drank before late afternoon, except when he was at the lake, and I knew that with my terrible remark about going there in August I'd driven him to taking a drink that morning. I would have to be more careful. He was mine to take care of now.

I hoped Aunt Helen hadn't noticed the glass with ice still in it standing on the tray. You had to protect your problems from her or she took them over.

I carried the tray to the kitchen and put the drink things away. I put Daddy's unused cigar back in the humidor, hoping it would get moist again, and noticing just where I placed it so I wouldn't get the same one out for him that afternoon. When I had dusted, the living room looked nice, ready for my father to come into.

As I did my work, I wondered if my aunt really thought she'd won. Did she really think I was going to let a housekeeper come into my house? Could she be that dense? Did her own strong personality make her overlook the fact that I had a will of my own? She'd find out that when she was dealing with me she wasn't dealing with the weakling her son, Harry, had turned out to be.

Chapter 7

❧❧❧❧❧❧❧❧❧❧❧❧❧❧❧❧❧❧

That evening, while I was getting ready to go with my father to the Stevensons' for dinner, I wished there weren't grass stains on my pink sheath. It would have been perfect to wear. But I put on my white linen suit and my white pumps, and with my hair in the French swirl no one would have guessed how young I was. When I was ready, I knocked on Daddy's door.

"Come in," he called.

"You're not ready yet," I said, surprised, because he'd had plenty of time. He was lying on the bed in his tan slacks and brown sport shirt. He hadn't even shaved.

"I'm ready any time you are," he said.

I felt terribly hurt. So many times I'd heard my mother say to him, "Jimmy, you really don't have to dress up tonight. It's too hot. You don't need a tie."

And invariably his answer was, "Look, honey, when I go stepping with my best girl, I dress up. See?"

But he wasn't dressing up for me. I wanted to be everything to him. I wanted to cook for him and clean house for him and be the girl he dressed up for.

I went to my mother's dressing table and started to touch my ears with her Tabu perfume.

"Dorie," he said, and his voice sounded as though he were wounded, "don't do that."

I kept my voice steady. "All right, Daddy," I said. Was her

perfume so precious that I couldn't use it? Because I was hurt, I felt an instant's bitterness toward my father. Then I realized what my mother was doing. Even dead, she was coming between us. That had always been her game, and she'd been so clever, he'd never seen through her for an instant.

But she is dead now, I told myself. And now I'm going to win. It may take time, but I'm going to win.

"I'll be downstairs, Daddy," I said. "Shall I fix you a drink?"

He sat up on the edge of the bed, his head in his hands. "Yes, honey, I'd like that," he said.

When I had the drink ready, I called him. He drank almost half of it at a gulp. Then he went into the kitchen and, without measuring, poured in more scotch and drank that, too, faster than I'd ever seen him take a drink.

The Stevensons still lived on Maple Street where they'd lived when we first became friends. Their house was one of the larger ones, not little and cramped as ours had been. Through the years they'd often said, "We really ought to get rid of this place, just the two of us rattling around in it." But year after year they went on living there, and year after year we went back to Maple Street several times a month to see them. Actually I was eight or nine years old before I realized they weren't relatives of ours. They seemed like part of the family. I couldn't even remember when we hadn't known them.

As we drove toward Maple Street, I said to my father, "It's a beautiful evening, isn't it, Daddy?"

He answered with a yes, but the tone of his voice made it obvious he wasn't noticing the evening or me or anything around him. During the years when I'd dreamed of my mother's death, I hadn't known how he was going to be. I had seen the two of us enjoying being alone together, he enjoying it as much as I. I had seen us laughing and joking and talking. I had heard him say to me some of the things he used to say to my mother, like, "Really, dear, you're the only woman I've ever known who is never boring," and now I was boring him, talking about the weather and the beautiful evening. I would have to try harder. I would have to be more interesting than my mother had been, because she had had him first and was still in his mind.

We turned on Maple Street and drove past the little house where we had lived those first years. One of the elm trees had been cut down recently and the yard had an unbalanced look. A little boy was sitting on the stump of the tree, eating an ice-cream cone with the chocolate dribbling down his chin and onto his sun suit.

I hadn't been much older than he when I sat under that tree, trying to open a bottle of my mother's nail polish. It was one of the many bottles in the house I wasn't supposed to touch. People were always telling my mother what beautiful hands she had, and she spent hours manicuring her nails.

I pulled a chair over to her bureau and stood on it and slipped the bottle of nail polish into the pocket of my smock. Outside I worked and worked trying to open the bottle. I didn't know you were supposed to unscrew the top and I kept pulling at it. Gradually I must have worked it around. I was pulling very hard when, suddenly, the top came off. I had been pulling with all my might and nail polish whipped from the brush onto my face and into my eyes.

It stung terribly and I started screaming. I was screaming partly from pain but more because my eyes were going to be stuck shut and I was going to be blind. I would never see my father again. But then he was lifting me up and carrying me into the house. He put me into the bathtub and talked to me until I was still. He bathed my eyes with lukewarm water, and I wasn't blind and I could see him.

I looked at my father beside me in the car, wishing he looked more like himself, strong and handsome. He didn't even seem to be as tall as he had been only a week earlier. She had taken something of him with her.

We were barely out of the car when Dan and Virginia came out their front door and Virginia hugged us both and Dan shook my father's hand and gave me a little hug. We walked around their house to the patio in back. Virginia had gone all out to have things nice for us. She was using the brown linen tablecloth and napkins and the Mexican dishes that I'd loved since I was a little girl. The table set for four was more nicely balanced than when there were five of us. I sat down in one of the lawn chairs, thinking of the meal I would cook when we had the Stevensons over. I could cook as well as Virginia or my mother, and on some things I was better at it than they were. For several years, every Thursday, I had cooked our evening meal. My mother wanted to make a big thing out of teaching me, but I'd heard my aunt say, "Any fool who can read can cook," and I learned mostly from cookbooks.

Dan had the usual pitcher of martinis for Virginia and him and scotch for my father. I sipped my Seven-Up, looking ahead a year or two when I'd be having a real drink with them.

The row of poplars at the back of the Stevensons' lawn cast shadows across the patio. It was beginning to cool off and a little breeze was coming up. It was going to be a pleasant evening.

"Well, boy,"—Dan looked at my father—"how's it going?"

My father stared at his drink. "It's rough, Dan. I can't tell you how rough."

Dan's voice was quieter than I'd ever heard it. "I know, boy. I know," he said.

"The thing of it is"—my father was looking at Virginia—"I can't believe it. I just can't believe it."

"That's what everyone says," Virginia answered him. "There was no one more alive than Eleanore."

As though she hadn't spoken, my father went on, "I keep looking for her. I walk into the house and I think she's there. Someone comes to the door and I look up to see her. I feel her move in bed at night."

Dan's hand was clenched into a fist on the arm of his chair. "It's a shame. A dirty, God-damned rotten shame."

I sat listening to them, wondering how long the memorial service was to go on.

Virginia said, "When I think of all the couples I know who would be just absolutely delighted if something happened to the other one, it's more than I can understand. I just cannot understand why it had to happen to you two. Why, I always said you were a perfect couple. Just perfect."

I wanted to speak up. I wanted to say something, anything, to change the subject. I knew how to talk about a lot of things. I read the newspapers and the news magazines and I read more books in a week than any of them did in a month. I knew how to talk. But I also knew that nothing was going to keep them from carrying on about my mother.

I got up and went into the house and sat against the red leather hassock in the living room where I used to sit when I was a little girl. The room was on the east and already was darkened by twilight.

They wouldn't notice that I left the patio. They wouldn't miss me. They didn't include me in a foursome. They wouldn't miss me until they'd finished their drinking and were ready to sit down at the table. I was still little Dorrie to all of them. They weren't admitting me to their level. But the day would come when the four of us would be together and we wouldn't sit around talking about my mother.

I leaned against the hassock, thinking of all the hours I'd spent in that room. On either side of the fireplace were corner cupboards, and in one of them Virginia kept toys for children who came to visit. I'd been there so often when I was little that

I'd come to think of the toys as mine. I got up and opened the cupboard and took out the blocks and airplanes and the jar with the beads in it. The rag doll that I had rocked to sleep so many times was there, and now one eye was missing. That doll was more familiar to me, more a part of me, than anything I had at home in my own room, except my Teddy bear.

Once I had thought the rag doll was beautiful. It was almost as though it had been my baby and had grown older and looked different now. The way it had been with my mother and me. I had been a beautiful baby. One day when I was playing in my sandbox and Mrs. Blake came across the street to have coffee and gossip with my mother, they were sitting at the kitchen table and I could hear every word. I heard my mother's laugh, and then she said, "Dorrie was one of the most beautiful babies you ever saw. Lots of thick brown hair, those big brown eyes. I was so proud of her. But heavens, now that she's getting older—isn't it awful the way they change?"

I hadn't known before that I was ugly. Since then I've heard people say that sometimes very handsome people have the ugliest children.

I put the toys back in the cupboard and went into the dining room and looked in the mirror. The French roll was staying up beautifully, and in my white suit, with my mother's beads around my neck, I wasn't ugly. I wasn't ugly any more and I wasn't going to let any words that my mother said long ago make me think I was.

When I went back to the patio, they were still drinking. My father was slouched down in his chair, his hand over his eyes. He was talking and his words were blurring, and I knew he'd been drinking fast.

"I'll never get over it," he was saying. "Never. Never. I don't know why it couldn't have been me. I don't know why I was left."

Virginia said, "You have Dorrie, Jim. You have Dorrie to live for."

She was slurring her words, and as she set her martini glass on the table in front of her, she banged it so hard I thought it would break.

"Yes, I have Dorrie," my father said. And then he repeated it, "I have Dorrie," and his voice trailed away.

In a tone filled with self-pity Dan said, "Look at Ginny and me. All alone. Look how it would be if anything happened to one of us with neither chick nor child."

Dan got up unsteadily and poured the last of the martinis in his glass. He took my father's glass then and started fixing him another drink.

I said, "Virginia, shall I go ahead and put the food on?"

A little surprised, as though she'd forgotten we were going to eat, she said, "Why, yes, Dorrie. Go ahead. That's a good girl."

I lighted the candles. Then I went into the kitchen and took the casserole from the oven and set it on the table. In the refrigerator I found the salad. When I'd filled the water glasses, I said, "Everything's ready now."

None of them moved, and I had to tell them again. We ate without speaking. It was almost completely dark except for the light of the candles and the flicker of fireflies. The sound of locusts in the air helped blot out the gloomy silence.

Virginia stood up and said, "There's pie. I've got apple pie for you, Jim."

But she was so unsteady that I said, "I'll get it," and she didn't say yes or no; she just sat down.

I cleared the table and served the pie and coffee. Virginia was a good cook, and she liked to make apple pie for my father, but I didn't mind. More than once I'd heard him say to my mother, "Ginny's a good egg, but I swear, she doesn't have an oversupply of brains."

Later I blew out the candles and stacked the dishes in the sink. Then for a long time we sat in almost complete silence on the patio. Several times I thought of interesting things to say, but the short answers I got showed no one wanted to talk. I sat there, wishing my father would say it was time to go home to bed.

That was a switch for me. I had always hated bedtime. When I was little, I had to go to bed before it got dark. I used to lie in bed in my little room on Maple Street and look at the brown stains on the ceiling of my room and listen to my parents still up and moving around. My bedroom had no door to it, but I couldn't have felt more shut away from them if there had been a door between us closed and barred and locked.

My mother looked forward to getting rid of me at night. Lots of times I heard her say, "When we get Dorrie to bed, let's ask the Stevensons over for cards," or, "As soon as I get her to bed, I'm going to cut out that pattern. I don't like to tackle it with her around."

She didn't put me to bed early because she wanted me to have the sleep. I didn't go to sleep. I stayed awake until long after they went to bed.

Sometimes after they put me to bed they ate something and didn't let me have any of it at all. It would get dark and I'd be lying there shut out and afraid, and then I'd smell shrimp boiling. I'd wish so much that my father would come into my room and say, "Come on and get up now, honey. Daddy's got some nice shrimp for his girl." But my mother, by talking a lot about children needing their sleep, kept him from doing it. The next morning when I got up, there'd be a couple of beer bottles standing on the drainboard and the smell of shrimp would still be in the kitchen.

Some time during the day Mrs. Blake would come over and my mother would say something like, "Jim and I had the best shrimp last night. We can't afford a sitter, but we do enjoy our midnight snacks."

With the way I was treated, it's no wonder that year after year I had nightmares. There was one particular dream that came back every once in a while, always exactly the same. In it I was walking along Maple Street with my father. The sun was shining and the birds were singing and the dandelions were blooming. My father held my hand. And then we came to the end of the block and there was a big pit there with two huge spits in it slowly turning around, inward toward each other, and I was going to fall into it. My father was gone, and I would wake up screaming.

My parents would rush into my bedroom and turn on the light and show me there was nothing to be afraid of. My mother would say, "She's wringing wet," and she'd change my nightgown and wipe my face with a damp cloth. My mother didn't want my father to stay with me. She'd say, "Go on back to bed, Jim. You need your sleep. I'll sit with her."

Then she'd turn out the light and put her hand on my arm or my shoulder and once in a while she'd pat me. But the terrible feeling stayed with me. It was my father who could have made it go away, but she didn't want that.

I don't know how I stood it in the years before I learned to read. But she didn't even want me to have that escape. I'd be in the living room, lying on my stomach, reading my first-grade reader, and I'd hear her say, "Is Dorrie in there reading again? That child has got to get out in the sunshine once in a while."

She'd put my sweater on me and make me go outside. There was nothing to do and I'd sit in my swing, just hanging on with one hand, waiting for time to pass. Sometimes she'd push my tricycle out the door and say, "Why don't you ride down to the end of the block and back, Dorrie? The exercise will do you good." Getting me out of the house didn't satisfy her. She wanted me out of the yard too.

The amazing thing was that no one, not one single person, saw through my mother. And this made me more alone than ever. People thought she was wonderful, and it wasn't until Sandy moved to town that I had anyone I could talk to.

The breeze had grown strong on the patio and in the west there was the flash of lightning.

I said, "Daddy, I think there's going to be a storm. Hadn't we better be getting home?"

He sighed and said, "Yes, baby, we better," and after a moment he pushed himself out of his chair and stood up.

The Stevensons walked with us to the car. By the time we were home it had started raining. I ran into the house and went about closing windows.

Then I said to my father, "How about a little snack, Daddy? I've got some Swiss cheese and rye."

But he said, "No, Dorrie, I've had enough for tonight. You go on up to bed."

I said, "I'm not sleepy, Daddy, really I'm not. I know I couldn't go to sleep yet."

He said, "It's time you were in bed. You go on now."

I kissed him good night and went slowly up the stairs. I undressed and climbed into bed and lay there listening for his footstep on the stair.

But pretty soon I heard him go out the front door and then I heard him start the car and drive off in the rain. I knew where he had gone. I wondered how long she would have his nights.

The terrible blackness came in on me. I was alone in the dark. I had no one. The only person I wanted was my father and I didn't have him.

I must have dozed then, because I was lying very stiff in bed, ready to spring out if the walls fell down. And then I was in the basement and black water bugs were running over me.

Chapter 8

The next morning I was awakened by the smell of coffee and I didn't like the thought of my father having to get up and take care of himself. From then on I would set the alarm. During the night the rain had stopped. The sun was shining, and the lonely feeling I'd had before I went to sleep was gone. I dashed water on my face, brushed my hair, and tied it back with a pink ribbon. I chose lipstick to match the ribbon, and the shorts and shirt I wore were crisp and clean. My father was not going to have to look at me in the mornings, puttering around in a robe and slippers.

He was standing at the kitchen counter, beating eggs in the small steel bowl.

"Good morning, Daddy," I said and kissed him. "Here, I'll do that."

"Hello, honey," he said. "I was going to let you sleep. We were pretty late last night."

I took the bowl from him and he went out in front and got the paper and sat at the kitchen table reading it, sipping a cup of coffee.

I turned a very low fire on under the skillet and cooked the eggs until the shine was almost gone. I spread lots of butter on the toast, just the way he liked it. Then I poured fresh coffee for both of us and said, "It's ready, Daddy." A thrill of happiness shot through me when he put down his paper and started to eat, without reading. That showed habits could be broken. Through the years he'd had to hide himself behind the paper to escape my mother's customary morning quiet.

"What shall we do today, Daddy?" I asked. "Would you like to go someplace or would you rather just rest?"

"I've had about all the rest I can take," he said. He got up and poured more coffee for us. "I've got to get back to the office. As it is, I've been out too long."

I was even happier. We were settling down to a normal routine. My father would go to the office every morning and come home to me every night. While he was gone, I would be getting the house and the dinner ready for him. I would plan our meals and go to the supermarket and buy our groceries. I would be very wise and careful with our money. He would see that there had been an extravagance through the years that he'd never suspected. From then on, money that my father worked so hard for would not be spent foolishly. His money represented him—his time, his effort, his energy. That had made no difference to my mother. I would think a long time before I let money go from his pocket into someone else's.

"Well, I've got work to do, too," I said. "For one thing, I want to get at my ironing."

"Don't try to do too much," he said. "Maybe we ought to send it out until we get a woman in for the housework."

"Oh no, Daddy," I said. "It won't be too much. We don't need anyone. I can do it easily, you'll see."

He said, "I can't have you burdened that way, baby. All of this is hard enough to get used to without saddling you with the housekeeping."

"But, Daddy, honest"—I could hardly keep my voice down —"I don't want anyone coming in. We don't want some stranger coming in and living with us."

"It can't be helped, Dorrie," he said. "There's no other way. God knows things are never going to be the same again."

And then I knew what to say. "Daddy, do you want someone

coming in, trying to take my mother's place? Do you really want that?"

He winced, and I almost wished I hadn't said it.

"No one will try to take her place," he said gently. "God knows, no one can do that."

He stood up then and said, "Let's not talk about it right now. We'll work something out."

I hadn't won, but I would. He went upstairs and I could hear the sound of his shaver, and I hummed while I put the dishes in the dishwasher.

When he came back, he had on his black silk suit and he was so handsome and beautiful that I hated to have him go downtown where all the good-looking secretaries and waitresses would be seeing him.

"How about coming home for lunch?" I asked him.

He said, "No, baby, there isn't time. You'll be all right. Call up one of your friends. Or, here." He took a couple of dollars from his billfold and put them on the hall table. "Get someone to go to a movie with you. It'll do you good."

I kissed him good-by, thinking of the groceries I would buy with the two dollars. Then I stood in the front door and watched him go to the car and drive off.

Although it was already warming up, I closed both doors and locked them. Then I went into my father's den and sat at his desk, organizing my day. There was going to be no more slipshod housekeeping in that house. I wrote down everything that needed to be done—the dusting, the vacuuming, bedmaking, ironing, picking fresh flowers. I studied the list then and wrote beside each chore a number showing the order of importance.

When my chore list was complete, I wrote my dinner menu. I would have T-bones, twice-baked potatoes with cheese, salad, and divinity. Divinity was my father's favorite candy, and I had worked at learning how to make it until I made it as well as my mother ever had. My father loved twice-baked potatoes, too, but my mother was so often out at card parties or doing volunteer work at the hospital until late in the afternoon, it was only on special occasions that she had fixed them for him. Now he would never have any other kind. Only his favorite.

I had just started making my father's bed when the phone rang. It was Sandy, wanting me to go swimming.

"I can't," I told her. "I've got all kinds of work ahead of me today. And anyway, if I have any time left, I'm going to look for the key."

"Oh, Dorrie," she said, "let me come and help look. I'll be real careful. Honest I will."

"No, Sandy," I said. "Thanks a lot, but you'd better not. I'll call you if I find it. I promise."

Once or twice, when my mother was gone, Sandy had helped me look for the key, but I'd had to go behind her, folding clothes and straightening drawers, and I'd wasted a lot of time that way.

And anyway, even Sandy was going to have to learn that there would be no more coming to the house until after I'd done my work. My mother had let neighbors and friends drop in any time they liked. She had encouraged it. "Come on in," she would say. "I was just going to have some coffee."

"I always feel at home here," people would tell her. "Your house is so warm and homey."

My house was going to be warm and homey, too, but it was going to be that way mainly for my father. Other people would be welcome only after I had everything ready for him.

He didn't realize how much he'd had to put up with—coming home at night and finding the table not even set and the living room undusted. He never complained. He was such a good sport that my mother took advantage of him.

She would look up and see him come in and say, "Hi, is it that late already? Heavens, I've let the day slip by me. I'm afraid I've spent too much time gabbing."

And he would kiss her and say, "That's all right, hon." He would smile his sweet smile and lay his cheek against hers and say, "I don't think any of us are very neglected around here."

Gradually, now, he would realize what it was to have a really well-run house. He would begin to see what he had been missing all that time.

I was starting to clean Daddy's bathroom when Aunt Helen's voice came cutting through the stillness like a knife.

"Dorrie, Dorrie," she called.

"Yes," I called back. "I'm coming. I'll be right down."

If I let her come up the stairs, she'd be that much harder to get rid of. And I simply did not have the time to let my aunt come running in every day. I carried the scouring powder and sponge down with me, hoping she'd see I was busy and leave soon.

She was in the kitchen, looking in the refrigerator.

"Are you hungry, Aunt?" I asked her, all eyes and innocent.

"Good gracious, no, I'm not hungry," she said. "I was just seeing how the food was holding out. What on earth did you do with it?"

"I put it down the disposal," I said. "We couldn't possibly eat all that stuff."

"But, Dorrie," she said, "you could have eaten some of it, and you could have given the rest away. It's sinful to waste good food."

I stood my ground. "I don't eat funeral food," I told her, "and I doubt if anyone would care to have me giving them funeral food."

She closed the refrigerator door and gave me a puzzled look.

"What a weird idea," she said and walked over to the stove and felt of the coffeepot. It was still hot, and she helped herself to a cup of coffee and reached for the sugar in the cupboard over the sink.

"Well, it's done now," she said. "I guess it really doesn't matter. Did your dad get back to work?"

"Yes," I said, "and I've got a lot to do before he comes home tonight."

Completely ignoring my words, she seated herself at the table and sipped her coffee.

I said, "Aunt, if you'll excuse me, I think I'll get back to my cleaning."

"Please sit down a moment, Dorrie," she said. "It's the cleaning I want to talk to you about. I've found someone, a woman who does housekeeping. She worked for years for Doc Brent, but now with him gone she's looking for something."

I pronounced each word clearly and distinctly. "But we do not need a housekeeper. We don't need anyone."

"Dorrie, Dorrie," she said reproachfully. "You sound as though I'm trying to harm you. Why, child, it's you I'm thinking of. You can't take on this housework at your age. School's going to be starting and you'll have your hands full with that. Now be reasonable, honey."

"But, Aunt," I said, "I am reasonable. I'm perfectly capable of taking care of my father and me. And I want to. Don't you understand?"

With one of her dramatic gestures, flinging her arms out, she said, "Honey, I understand that you're a good girl and you want to do everything you can to make things easier for your father. But you've got to think of yourself too."

She got up and rinsed out her cup and put it in the dishwasher. "No, no, it won't do," she said, as though everything were settled. "I'm going to ask Mrs. Mason to come over and talk to your father as soon as she can. We've got to get organized before school starts."

I set the scouring powder down on the table with a thump. "Do you think just anyone can take care of my father?" I asked her. My hands were shaking and my voice was loud. "Why, do you know that he couldn't even wear the shirts that you, yourself, ironed for him? I had to wash them all over and today I'm going to iron them myself. And I'll do it right too."

"Dorrie." Her voice was low and coaxing. "That isn't like you at all. You've gotten yourself all worked up about nothing."

She came over and put her arm around my shoulder, but I wrenched away from her.

"You're a busybody." I clenched my teeth to keep from yelling. "My mother always said you were better at minding other people's business than taking care of your own child."

She backed away a little and then sort of crumpled down into a kitchen chair. I grabbed the can of scouring powder from the table and marched out of the room and upstairs and sprinkled powder in Daddy's bathtub. My anger had given me too much energy, and I scrubbed the tub longer than necessary. I couldn't stop scrubbing and I couldn't stop seeing Aunt Helen sitting there at the kitchen table with that caved-in look on her face.

Finally I got rid of her. She was walking through a dark, deep forest. She wanted to get into the sunshine and she ran out into the center of a clearing. There was quicksand and it got harder and harder for her to walk, and finally she couldn't lift her feet. She began to sink in, sink in. The more she struggled, the faster she sank.

When the quicksand closed over her chest, she stopped struggling, and finally there was only her head left and then that, too, went under, the quicksand pushing her stiff hair up. Then even all trace of that peroxide hair was gone. I was glad she hadn't called to me while she was sinking. Sometimes my mother used to.

Later I heard my aunt go out the front door and I watched her through Daddy's window until she got into her car and drove away. Then I looked at my list and went to the yard to pick fresh bouquets of marigolds.

When Daddy came home that evening, everything was clean and shining and beautiful for him. His shirts were hanging in his closet, the top and middle button of each fastened, and all facing the same way. The table was set, and in the center I had placed an arrangement of marigolds and spiraea leaves. I had taken out my best china and crystal. No longer would it be used only for compnay. My father deserved to use it every day. I had colored the divinity a delicate pink and had it arranged in the silver dish. The clean smell of furniture polish was in the living room, and from the kitchen there came the fragrance of fresh coffee.

I was clean and beautiful, too, or at least I felt beautiful. I had washed my hair and brushed it dry and it was shiny and soft. As I was putting on my green jumper and white blouse and the Mexican sandals the Stevensons had brought me from California, I made a rule for myself that never would my father come home and find me in shorts or slacks.

I noticed right away how tired my father looked. He went straight to his chair and sat down and fixed himself a drink. He leaned back and sipped it, and then he looked across at me.

"Dorrie," he said, "your aunt called me today."

"Oh?" I said, wondering what she'd told him.

"She's worried about you. She says you're more upset than I realize at the idea of our getting a housekeeper."

"We don't need one, Daddy," I said.

"I know that's the way you feel." He set his glass down. "But, listen now, honey. This isn't something for you to decide. Whether you like it or not, we've got to have help."

I didn't say anything. My father was speaking to me as though I were a child and it was all my aunt's doing. With every bit of strength I had I hated her.

My father went on. "There's a Mrs. Mason who's going to call. If she seems all right, I want to try her out, for a week or two at least. Now I want you to promise me that when she comes you'll try to like her."

If my father wanted my promise, I couldn't refuse to give it to him. And my word was as good as the person I gave it to. I never broke a promise to my father.

"All right, Daddy," I said, "I promise. I'll try to like her."

"That's all I ask, baby," he said. "Just try."

As I went into the kitchen to put the T-bones under the broiler, I hated Aunt Helen almost as much as I had hated my mother. The bone-handled knife was on the counter and I picked it up and hated my aunt. Finally I put it in the knife rack where it belonged.

The T-bones were almost ready to turn when the telephone rang. I went to the den and picked it up.

"Hello," I said.

The voice was a soft woman's voice. "This is Mrs. Mason. Is Mr. Lawson there, please?"

I said, "You must have the wrong number."

I had just started turning the steaks when the telephone rang again. I didn't answer it this time. I heard my father say hello and I thought of how she must be feeling to hear his lovely deep voice coming across the wire to her.

Then he said, "Why, yes, yes, I'd be very glad if you could, Mrs. Mason. About seven-thirty, then. All right. Good-by."

He fixed himself another drink and brought it into the kitchen.

"Mrs. Mason will be over a little later this evening," he said. "Now remember, honey, what you promised Daddy."

"I'll remember," I said.

Chapter 9

ꙮꙮꙮꙮꙮꙮꙮꙮꙮꙮꙮ

She stood at the door, and in the same soft voice I'd heard on the telephone she said, "Is this the Lawson residence? I'm Mrs. Mason."

I said yes and invited her in. I gestured toward the living room and said, "My father's in there."

As she walked past me, I noticed she had a bad limp and then I saw her clubfoot. The gray dress she wore was long, but not long enough to hide it. She had on ugly black shoes, and one shoe was built up especially for her. It scraped a little on the floor as she walked.

My father had been on the sofa, taking a nap, and now he stood up and held out his hand to her.

"This is my daughter, Dorrie," he said, and I, too, shook her hand.

She sat down in Daddy's chair and I sat beside him on the sofa.

"I hear you're looking for someone," she said.

She and my father talked then, not saying anything very much. Mainly they were sizing each other up. I sat there and looked her over and tried to like her. Her voice was nice, but it didn't go with the rest of her at all. She was old, older than my father, even older than Aunt Helen. She was small and wiry and clean and neat, but she wasn't pretty and she never had been. Actually she was ugly, except when she smiled. I had found two things to like, her voice and her smile, which was shy and a little bashful. I reminded myself that it couldn't have been easy for her, being crippled that way. Maybe I could like her for that too. There must have been many times when she'd been shut out.

After a while my father said, "Well, Mrs. Mason, let's give it a try. What do you say to coming in for a week? We'll see how everything works out. If you like us and we like you, then we'll make permanent arrangements."

"Yes, sir, I'd like that," she said. "I can come in the forenoon tomorrow."

My father turned to me. "Dorrie, show Mrs. Mason her room. It'll give her some idea of what to bring with her."

I led the way upstairs and noticed she was able to climb the steps surprisingly fast, even though her clubfoot banged against each step. Her room was the spare one at the head of the stairs, and she followed me in and looked around and said, "It's nice. It's real nice."

She went over to the window then and looked out and said something about our yard being pretty. I stood waiting for her to go ahead of me from the room. She did, but as she went by me, she stopped and lightly touched my cheek with her hand. "I had a little girl once," she said.

When she had gone, my father said, "Well, Dorrie, what do you think? Do you think you can get along with her?"

"I'm trying to like her, Daddy," I told him. "There are three things I can like already. She has a nice smile, and her voice is nice. And then there's her foot too."

My father smiled tenderly at me, and I was so happy that I was more determined than ever to like Mrs. Mason.

"I know what you mean, baby, about the foot," he said. "What a terrible handicap! But the poor thing gets around well."

When my father smiled at me, I realized that he had hardly smiled at all since he came home from the hospital, and not once had I heard him laugh. This was the sound I liked best in the world; he never laughed unless he really felt like it. That was why he never sounded phony like other people. I was lonesome to hear him laugh, but he had smiled, and laughing would come.

But now the smile was gone and he was serious and tired-looking again. He said, "I think we'd better go over and spend some time with Grandma tonight. Helen says she's feeling pretty low."

"I'll take her some divinity," I said. I knew that because of her false teeth she wouldn't be able to eat it, but she could pass it out to visitors, and I hoped my thoughtfulness would make my father smile again. But he didn't seem to have another smile in him that night.

Grandma lived across town, not too far from my aunt's house. She was sitting out on her front porch in her rocker, not rocking, just sitting there staring across the street. She saw us stop and she stood up and held on to the porch railing, peering into the street, but her eyes were getting worse all the time and you had to be up pretty close before she could see you.

"It's us, Grandma," my father called.

She smiled, but then her smile cracked into crying and my father put his arms around her as though she were a little girl and held her close to him.

"There, there," he said. "Come on now, Lizzie, that's the girl."

She let up a little and he got a clean white handkerchief from his pocket and wiped her face very gently with it.

Then he tried the old joke, but his voice wasn't happy when he said it. "We can't have the best-looking grandmother in town carrying on like this."

My grandma tried to smile, but she didn't want consolation and tears started squeezing out of her eyes again.

"Come here, Sister," she said to me, and I held still while she gave me one of her hugs.

"Here's some candy, Grandma," I said and handed her the aluminum-foil-wrapped package.

We all sat on the porch then, Daddy and I in the swing and Grandma in her rocker. She talked on and on, telling Daddy about the funeral flowers and the singing. As usual she repeated herself a lot, but my father was far too kind to let on he noticed.

Then she went clear back to the time when my grandfather died and Aunt Helen was only twelve and my mother was six and Grandma was left to support them alone. I knew it all by heart, word for word, sigh for sigh.

She always ended it with, "But we made out. I don't say it wasn't hard. But I had two good girls, such good girls. Why, while I worked, Helen looked after Eleanore like she was her mother."

"I know, Lizzie," my father said. "Eleanore never forgot it either. She thought there was no one like Helen."

"Oh yes, they thought the world of each other," Grandma went on. "They were always close. What happened to one happened to the other."

"Yes," my father said, giving the swing a push. "When Harry got into trouble, Eleanore felt it as much as Helen. You'd have thought he was her son. Through it all Eleanore kept saying that the only thing wrong with him was that Helen had given him too much, that except for that she was a perfect mother. She always did say he'd come out of it."

That started Grandma off on Harry, and she sat there telling my father the whole story about the arrest and everything, as though he didn't already know it. I was tired of listening and I got up and walked around to the back yard and sat on one of the lawn chairs under the pear tree. Some of the pears had already dropped and bees were buzzing around them.

In our back yard on Maple Street there had been a big old walnut tree. My father would gather up the walnuts and knock the hulls off them and then wash them nice and clean. He'd store them in bushel baskets in the basement, and lots of nights after school I'd go down there and get a handful of them and take them to the kitchen to crack. He showed me how to spread a newspaper out on the floor first and then put the red brick in the middle and how to clean up the mess when I'd finished. I always did it just the way he said.

One evening after school I invited Jackie Talbot to come home with me. She had naturally curly hair and, next to me, was the best reader in second grade. She was good at jumping rope, too, and we were going to be best friends. She lived three blocks from me, and we stopped there on the way home from school and her mother said she could stay at my house until five o'clock.

On the way we traded coats. I turned the sleeves of hers wrong side out and buttoned it under my chin and wore it like a cape. We skipped down the street and I was happy because I had a friend.

My mother was in the kitchen ironing. She smiled at us and wanted to know if we would like some cookies and milk.

I said, "No, I'm going to get some of Daddy's walnuts."

I took a pan and went down the basement stairs. I could reach the nuts from the bottom step. Because of the water bugs I never went clear into the basement.

After I had everything fixed in the kitchen and Jackie and I were taking turns cracking nuts, my mother came over to us and rubbed her hand through Jackie's hair and said, "It's naturally curly, isn't it, Jackie? It's just beautiful." I was proud because my best friend's hair was beautiful.

My mother finished her ironing and said she was going to run over to Mrs. Blake's for a while and for us to be good girls. Pretty soon my father came home and out into the kitchen, and he patted my head and then he patted Jackie's head too. He took a bottle of beer out of the refrigerator and opened it and sat at the kitchen table drinking it.

Jackie hit a walnut and it skittered, unbroken, across the room and bounced against the wall.

"Jackie Lantern," my father said, "that's not the way to crack nuts."

He was smiling at her and she was smiling back at him, trying to look prettier than she really was. She giggled and repeated "Jackie Lantern" after him.

He looked at her as though he thought she was very pretty and awfully cute. Then he looked at me, still smiling the same smile, but I knew the smile had started out being for her. I slammed the hammer down on my thumb. Daddy took me on his lap and patted me and tried to get me to stop crying, but I couldn't, and finally he said, "You better run on home now, Jackie. You can come back soon."

The next day in school I acted as though I didn't hear when she tried to whisper to me. And from then on I walked home from school a different way, not going by her house any more. One night about a week later, without even being invited, she came to our front door, and I went and opened the door and said, "I don't want to play," and I slammed it shut. I never did have a friend again until Sandy moved to town.

It had grown dark and the bees had stopped buzzing and fireflies had come out. When I was little, I used to catch fireflies and mash off their lighted parts and press them against my fingers for rings. My mother, pretending to be more tenderhearted than I, would say, "Dorrie, please, for heaven's sake, put them in a jar if you want to, but don't do that. It's cruel." I got up and walked back to the porch where my father and Grandma were, remembering the metallic smell of the smashed fireflies.

As I came around the corner of the house, my father was

telling Grandma we'd come over another time to look at pictures. One of the things she liked best was to corner you and make you sit and look while she pointed out dead people in the family album.

On the way home I wondered if my father would drop me off when we got there and then go on out to my mother's grave. I figured he would, so I said, "Daddy, would you mind taking me to the cemetery?"

He patted my knee and said, "Of course not, honey. I didn't mention it before because you've been holding up so well. I was afraid it would depress you."

We drove the short distance out of town and through the high gates and up the hill near my mother's grave. There was faint moonlight and I could see that someone had put strips of sod over the fresh earth, but it was drying up and not growing. My father and I walked together to the grave and then he knelt and left me standing there alone.

That was an old trick of hers, to separate us. I began to wonder if I'd made a terrible mistake in imagining her death for so long. Maybe what I should have imagined was her doing something that would completely alienate her from my father. My father had his head bowed, quiet, silent, not knowing I was there. I started to imagine her falling in love with another man and running away, but I didn't go on with it. In the first place, it was too hard to imagine her forgetting my father, and in the second place, it wouldn't do any good. She was already dead.

After a long time my father stood up and started walking back to the car, his head down, not noticing whether or not I followed him. But at least he wouldn't be going out later that night. He had already been with her.

I remembered to set my alarm that night, and after I'd undressed and was ready for bed, I went into my father's room to kiss him good night. He was in the bathroom, urinating. I was reminded of the years when I'd thought he had several penises, and the thought made me smile.

That night I dreamed that my mother and my father and I were at the beach, having a picnic. My father and I were dressed for swimming, but my mother was menstruating and she had on a long gray dress just like Mrs. Mason's.

My father took us near the edge of the water. Then he spread out a blanket and my mother smoothed it carefully until all the wrinkles were out of it. I picked up the picnic hamper and set it on the blanket and my mother knew I was very hungry. She said, "Don't be greedy, Dorrie. There's more than one drumstick."

I was so hungry I could hardly stand it and I sat down on the sand away from the blanket. Then I heard music. It wasn't particularly beautiful, but its rhythm was strong. I started moving in time to it and then I stood up and held out my arms to my father and said, "Dance with me, Daddy."

My father took me in his arms and we danced away across the sand. Sometimes we danced very close to the water, but I wasn't afraid. The music ended and we walked exactly in step, arm in arm, back to the blanket. My mother was gone, and I smoothed the blanket carefully and got all the wrinkles out of it. My father squatted down and heaped sand up until it made a little wall all the way around and people could tell that this certain spot was ours.

We sat down together and I started to take food out of the hamper. My father said, "I forgot to give you your prize for dancing."

He held out his pen to me, and I opened my purse and he slipped it inside.

The dream was so wonderful that it woke me up in the night and I had to go to the bathroom. Afterward I went into the hall and stood looking for a long time at my father asleep in the moonlight.

Chapter 10

It was too bad I went back to sleep that night, because the next morning, the wonderful feeling which the dream had given me was gone. I woke up with the premonition that something terrible was going to happen. Then I remembered. The housekeeper was coming that day. And I had made a promise to my father.

As I dressed, I said over and over to myself, "I am going to like Mrs. Mason." But when I was in the kitchen and started making the coffee, I couldn't keep from knowing that this was the last breakfast I would fix for my father. I fried bacon and scrambled eggs and made blueberry muffins. I poured a cup of coffee and took it upstairs. Daddy was just waking up and he reached for the coffee and said, "That's just what I need. Thanks, honey."

I took his robe from the closet and held it for him. When he had washed, we went downstairs together. As we ate, the words "the last breakfast" kept going through my mind.

Some Saturdays Daddy didn't have to go to the office, but because he'd missed so much work he was behind and had to go on this Saturday. When I had kissed him good-by, I watched him go down the front walk. When he was almost to the car, I called to him.

He stopped and turned around. "Yes, Dorrie?" he said.

I smiled at him and said, "I'm going to try hard to like Mrs. Mason."

"I know you will, baby," he said. He waved at me then, and I watched until his car was out of sight.

While I washed the dishes and made the beds, I tried to think of the best way to make myself like Mrs. Mason. Then I remembered my first piano recital. I had been terribly afraid that I would make a mistake or forget my piece and I told my father that I was.

He said, "Just don't let on. Walk out on that platform as if you didn't have a care in the world. Acting as if you aren't afraid will help you not be."

Daddy had been right and it had worked. Maybe it would work the same way with liking someone. If I acted as though I liked her, maybe I would like her. Then I tried to think of what I would do if I really did like her. That was easy. I started imagining that it was my father who was coming to live in the room at the head of the stairs.

I went out to my row of marigolds and picked a beautiful bouquet of them. I arranged them carefully in a dark green vase and took them upstairs to Mrs. Mason's room. I put some of the divinity on a saucer, covered it with a square of waxed paper, and placed it on her bedside table. I took my own little radio and put it on her bureau and plugged it in. But her bureau looked too bare, and I took the serape off mine and put it on hers. I was downstairs looking for a wastebasket to put in her room when the doorbell rang.

She was at the door, holding a big suitcase in one hand. In the other she had a package wrapped in newspaper. I smiled at her as though I liked her very much. I held open the screen door, and when she limped through it, I took her suitcase and the package, too, although she kept saying, "No, no, you mustn't."

I carried the things upstairs and she came along behind, her clubfoot hitting against the steps. I set her suitcase down and put her package on the bed. She looked at the marigolds and touched one of them.

"These are real pretty," she said. "Did you grow them?"

"Yes," I said, "and I picked them for you."

She gave me a smile and said, "I've always liked marigolds. They're one of my favorite flowers."

I wished she hadn't said it. It was all too obvious that Aunt Helen had tipped her off to pretend she liked them. But I stopped my thoughts right there. If I let what Aunt Helen had done influence me, I wouldn't be able to keep my promise.

I said, "Would you like a cup of coffee?"

She said, "Why, yes, child, that would be real nice. Just as soon as I get unpacked."

But I went downstairs right then and fixed coffee and cream and sugar on a tray and took it up to her.

She said, "Why, Dorrie, how good of you. But you're spoiling me. I came to do for you, you know."

She looked at me as though she liked me very much. I thought of telling her that she had it mixed up. She didn't have to like me; I had to like her. But instead I uncovered the divinity and offered her a piece.

I didn't stay around to watch her unpack. Aunt Helen, with her one-track mind, would keep on insisting that she go through my mother's things and get rid of them. But before she did I had to find the key.

I said, "Mrs. Mason, I think I'll go in my father's room and read a while."

She said, "You go on, child. I'll be all right." She set down her coffee cup and looked at me and said, "We're going to get along fine, Dorrie. I can tell that already."

I was part way out of the door when she said, "Child, what do you like to eat? What would you enjoy for dinner?"

I said, "My father likes beef better than anything, steaks and roasts." I hated to go on, but I did. "And he likes twice-baked potatoes and apple pie and divinity."

I felt as though I'd given her something that it wasn't right to give, something that I wanted back.

"And what do you like?" she asked.

"The same," I said and went down the hall to my room and got a book and then went into my father's room.

I leaned the book against the door so I wouldn't forget to take it with me when I left. Then I started the search. I was careful and methodical. I kept the eight divisions of the room in mind. One by one I emptied drawers and removed the paper linings. I shook out each garment before I folded it and replaced it. I felt at the back of drawers and looked under them. A key could be tacked to anything. I moved the bureau out from the wall and examined the back of it. I unmade the bed and took the box springs off. I was just ready to start on the closet when Mrs. Mason called me to lunch.

It was amazing how fast she'd become used to my kitchen. She had the table set and soup and salad and pudding ready. On the counter she had placed a beef roast, thawing for the evening meal. She had made herself terribly at home. She had taken over. I realized I wasn't liking her, and it hurt my feelings to think I was failing Daddy.

I smiled at her and said, "Oh, I love soup, Mrs. Mason, and chocolate pudding is one of my favorite foods."

Her face looked as though I'd given her a present. When we had eaten, I left the kitchen to go on with the search. As I walked up the stairs, I could hear her humming while she cleared the table.

The sound of her humming in my kitchen stayed in my ears. I opened my mother's closet door. But the humming was with me and I stood there doing nothing. Mrs. Mason limped along the edge of a cliff. Down below there were huge boulders and dashing waves. She was getting closer and closer to the edge. There were rocks in her way, and her clubfoot scraped them along ahead of her. She was very close to the edge.

I stopped just in time. I threw myself on my father's bed and cried. The promise was so hard to keep.

I couldn't stop crying as fast as I wanted to. I was thinking that I would get up and wash my face when I heard someone coming up the stairs. My father opened the door and stood there a moment. Then, looking sad and almost sick, he came over and sat down on the bed.

"Go ahead and cry, baby," he said. "You have a right. God knows, you have a right."

Then he hunched over with his face in his hands and I was afraid I'd made him start crying. But in a moment he looked up and out the window, and as though he were talking to himself, he said, "Only a week. My God, it's only been a week."

My father turned toward me then and grasped my shoulder so hard it hurt, but I didn't care. He said, "One thing I'm glad of, baby. You had her through most of your childhood. No one can take that away from you."

I couldn't answer him. It was as though he had spoken to me in a foreign language.

He got up and took off his suit coat and hung it in his closet. Then he said, "I believe I'll take a nap, Dorrie. I'm not sleeping right at night."

He stood there by the bed, and I could see he was waiting for me to get up and leave him alone. I would have liked to stay.

Mrs. Mason was standing at the kitchen sink peeling potatoes paper-thin. At least she wasn't wasting my father's money.

"Mrs. Mason," I said, "my father's resting. Don't let anyone bother him. If there are any phone calls, I'll take them."

"All right, Dorrie," she said. "That's a good idea. I know he's been through a lot."

"And I wouldn't even go upstairs while he's asleep," I went

on. "He's a very light sleeper." It wasn't possible for her to go up the stairs quietly.

She limped over to the refrigerator and stood with her hand on the door. "Couldn't I fix you a coke?" she asked.

I started to say no, but then I remembered my promise. "You sit down and rest a bit," I said. "I'll fix one for each of us."

"No, no, child, let me do it." She started to take the cokes from the refrigerator, but I took them from her and got out ice and fixed two tall glasses for us.

She sat across the table from me, again looking as though she liked me very much. She sipped her coke and said, "I never knew your poor mother, but just from knowing you, she must have been a wonderful person."

Again I was left without an answer. I smiled at her and tried to make my eyes look as if I liked her. I tried to feel as if I liked her.

"What kind of cake do you like best?" she asked me.

"My father and I both like chocolate," I told her.

She didn't sit long after that. She got up and took eggs and butter from the refrigerator. When she set out the bitter chocolate, I knew what we were going to have for dessert. It hurt me to watch her doing my work, so I tiptoed upstairs to my room.

I lay on the bed for a while, thinking about my mother's locked drawer. Maybe I'd find letters from a lover that she'd kept hidden from us. I went back over the men we'd known, trying to imagine each of them meeting my mother secretly and writing passionate letters to her. But I couldn't see it. She had my father. It wasn't likely she'd fool around with any other man.

Maybe I'd find something that would explain why people never had seen through her. Maybe I'd find proof of what she was really like.

I got up and took my library book from the bureau and

turned on the duck lamp and sat down in my rocker. My grandma had given the rocker to me when I was five years old, and it was the only piece of furniture in my room which we had kept when we moved from Maple Street. My great-grandfather had brought it across the prairie in a covered wagon, and my grandma never let me forget it. My mother had made yellow chintz pads for it when she redecorated my room.

The furniture we'd had on Maple Street was mostly dingy and broken down and fitted the dreariness of the house. When we moved away from there, things were a lot different. We bought new furniture and the new house was big and light compared to the old one. I went to a different school, and I'll never forget the first day when I had to walk up the long sidewalk to the schoolhouse and all the kids stopped playing and stared at me.

When we were settled in the new house, my father bought a piano and my mother asked me if I wanted to learn how to play it. I told her that I did. I thought that someone would come to the house once or twice and show me how to do it and from then on I'd be able to play. But my mother, in her usual way, hadn't told me she meant that for years I'd be taking piano lessons. The lessons and practicing and recitals started and went on and on. When I'd complain, she'd say, "Now, Dorrie, you wanted lessons and you've got them. You just go right in there and start practicing."

Even though the new house was lighter and more cheerful, part of the gloom from Maple Street came with me. My mother went on being just the way she always had been. And somehow the black water bugs and the house falling in kept coming into my dreams. And I was still outside the bubble.

I couldn't get interested in my library book but it wasn't long before I heard Daddy moving around and I washed and put on my pink blouse and skirt and my turquoise beads. When I went downstairs, Daddy was in the kitchen saying something about the weather to Mrs. Mason. She was frosting the cake, not turning around, just barely answering him. She looked at me and said, "That pink is real pretty on you, Dorrie. It's your color."

And later, while we ate dinner, everything was Dorrie. It was almost as though she didn't know my father was there. "Do you want some more meat, Dorrie?" "Would you like some catsup?" "Did you enjoy your reading this morning?" My father seemed pleased enough to have her do the talking, but I wondered. Was her indifference to him a pose? Could she really be that unaware that she was sitting at the table with my father?

It took me a long time to figure her out, and when finally I did, it changed everything. I hated what I had to do, not while I was doing it, but later, and lots of times now she's all mixed up in my dreams. Sometimes I wonder if you can ever really get rid of a person. Sometimes I think that you carry around with you all of the time everyone you've ever known.

Chapter 11

As the days went by I found that gradually I stopped trying to like Mrs. Mason and really began to like her. It would have been hard not to, the way she treated me. Nothing seemed to make her happier than to be doing something for me. It wasn't actually, though, so much what she did as it was the way she felt about me. And though I watched her closely at first, I could see she had no designs whatever on my father. He hardly existed for her.

One evening I went out the front door and around the house on my way to the park. I hadn't wanted to go through the kitchen because Mrs. Berkson was there and I didn't want to get hung up talking to her. As I went past the window, I heard my name and stepped to one side to listen.

Mrs. Berkson was speaking. "Yes, she's a dear child," she said. "I've watched her grow up and you can't tell me anything about her. She's smart as a whip too. Always on the honor roll."

Mrs. Mason spoke. "And she's so . . . well, I've only been here two weeks now, but she's such a loving child. She made me feel right to home. I just fell in love with her."

And it wasn't only that she really liked me—lots of people liked me—but she *admired* me and, what was more, liked nothing better than to brag about me to my father. This was such a change from the way my mother had acted, complaining and telling on me every time she had a chance. Mrs. Mason and my father and I would be sitting at the dinner table and she'd say to him, "Have you noticed how pretty Dorrie looks in her new blouse?" or, "Mr. Lawson, I do pride myself on being a fair cook, but I can't take credit for this pie. Dorrie made it, and its as good as I've ever tasted."

My father seemed pleased to have her there. I heard him say one evening to Virginia, "We hit the jack pot with this housekeeper. She's a good cook and she's taken a real liking to Dorrie. Actually she's a very motherly soul."

One evening, not long before school started, I said to my father, as I had several times on other evenings, "Daddy, let's play cards."

And as usual he said, "I'm bushed, baby. Mrs. Mason might like to play, though."

Mrs. Mason was in the dining room wiping the table and she said, "I'll play, Dorrie, if you promise not to beat me again." I didn't promise, but I opened the gate-legged table and shuffled the cards, thinking I'd play a hand or two with her. We had just started when the Stevensons came.

Dan was even louder than usual and both of them were bubbling over with their news. Dan was being sent to Chicago to a three-day convention, and they were both going to go and make a one-week vacation out of it.

"And," Virginia said, looking at my father, "we've got the most marvelous idea! You've got to come too! Now don't say no. It's just what you need, to get away from here for a while."

"What do you say, boy?" Dan boomed out. "How about it?"

"Why, I don't know," my father said. "I've got some time coming, but I don't know that I ought to leave."

Nobody had mentioned me until Mrs. Mason spoke up, and then I could have hit her.

"If it's Dorrie you're thinking of," she said, "don't worry about leaving her." She smiled and added, "I'll take care of her like she was my own."

"But I'd go, too," I said then, my voice coming out almost as loud as Dan's. "Wouldn't I, Daddy? If you went, I'd go."

"Why, honey," my father said, "I don't see how you could miss the beginning of school."

"I could," I said. "I could miss a week and never even know it."

"No, I'm afraid that wouldn't do," he said. "You know how your mother felt about good attendance—and she was right. I couldn't keep you out of school."

Mrs. Mason didn't say anything more and neither did I. The Stevensons kept pointing out reasons my father should go with them, but it ended with his saying, "I don't know. I'll have to think it over."

A couple of nights later I was in my room reading. I heard my father come back from the cemetery, and when he came upstairs he knocked on the door of my room.

He sat down in my rocker and then he told me he'd decided to go with the Stevensons. He'd checked it out at the office and it was all right there, and he felt the change would be good for him.

"What about me?" I asked.

He smiled and said, "Honey, I'm not worried about you at all—not with Mrs. Mason looking after you. I've never seen two people take to each other the way you two have. You'll have a fine time right here with her."

I looked down at the floor, not saying anything.

He said, "Now don't pout, honey. Surely you must realize how lucky we are to have Mrs. Mason. It's been a great load off my mind to have you taken care of."

My father was turning me over to her! He was glad to. And that was what she wanted. She wanted me to be her little girl. And my father would go to Chicago and leave me.

When my father had gone to his room, I undressed for bed, knowing that Mrs. Mason had to go. The question was, how to get rid of her. I lay for a long time, thinking, and then I got up and dressed quickly and dialed Sandy's number. Sandy was under the bridge when I got to the park, and I told her everything.

"How am I going to get rid of her?" I finally asked.

"Could you scare her some way?" Sandy said.

I sat, considering it. I might get up in the night and make noises, but if I did, my father would hear them, and anyway, I had the feeling she'd be hard to scare. Maybe I could pretend to have some kind of a fit. There had been a boy at school who did, and it had scared a lot of people. But the minute I thought of it I knew it was a bum idea. It would just make her want to take care of me.

"I don't think scaring her's a very good idea," I finally said.

Sandy wanted to know if I wanted a cigar, but I needed to think so I told her I was going on home. I said, "I'll see you," and as she always did, she answered, "See you," and we left each other.

All through the next day I did almost nothing except try to think of a good way to get rid of Mrs. Mason. I went to my room early that evening and sat in my rocker and concentrated. It grew dark and I undressed and put on my nightgown. The street lights came on and there were fireflies in the yard, and later I heard the nine-o'clock whistle blow.

After a while I heard her thump, thumping down the stairs, and shortly afterward she came back up again and down the hall to my bedroom door. She knocked and in her soft voice called my name.

Without opening the door I said, "Yes?"

She said, "I brought you a bite to eat before bedtime."

I opened the door and she was standing there with a glass of milk and a huge slice of chocolate cake.

"I know how girls like snacks," she said, as she had almost every other evening she'd been there. She smiled that sincere-looking smile of hers and said, "Good night, now. Sleep tight."

I took the cake and milk and said thank you, and she turned and limped down the hall. She looked so happy—almost as if she thought she were in a bubble with me—that I felt sorry for her. I didn't want to feel sorry for her. I thought of how she had taken over my kitchen and cooked such good meals for my father. I thought of how she wanted me to be her little girl and how my father was willing to turn me over to her. I poured the milk down the toilet and set the cake on the bureau.

I climbed into bed, but it was a long time before I went to sleep. At first I was still trying to figure out what I would do. Then I drifted into something like sleep and I was on Maple Street and the walls of the house had fallen down and I was in the basement and black water bugs were running over me. I was pinned down by something big and black and ugly. As I struggled awake, I knew the thing holding me down was Mrs. Mason's awful built-up shoe.

I woke up afraid of Mrs. Mason. I wished I had a key for my door and could lock myself in. I got up and put my straight chair to the door and wedged it under the handle. It was a long time before I fell asleep again.

I slept late the next morning, and when I went downstairs my father was in the kitchen with Mrs. Mason, drinking coffee and looking at the paper.

He gave me a weary smile, and in a voice that he was trying to make cheerful he said, "Well, good morning, sleepyhead."

I kissed him and put my cheek against his.

Smiling at me, Mrs. Mason wanted to know what I would like for breakfast. They'd already eaten.

I said, "Thanks, but I'll get my own."

I took a piece of cheese from the refrigerator.

She said, "Wouldn't you like some bacon or a nice piece of ham?"

I said, "No, thanks, Mrs. Mason. Cheese is very nutritious."

She looked a little worried, but she didn't say anything. Looking at her, I was surprised that I'd been afraid of her in the night. Actually she only looked beaten down and old. But I felt uneasy around her and I wanted to get out of the house. It was Sunday and a beautiful day. I remembered how my father acted when I'd asked him if we'd be going to the lake during August. I wondered if I dared suggest we go somewhere that day.

Finally I said, "Daddy, do you think we could have a picnic today?"

He wasn't angry; he just said no. "I'm not up to it," he said. "I'm going out to the cemetery and then I've got some things I want to do here at home. I'm sorry, Dorrie."

Before I could tell him it was all right, Mrs. Mason said, "My nephew's coming for me this afternoon. He lives on a farm out of town. Would you like to go with me, Dorrie? They've got horses."

My father said, "Why don't you go along, baby? Things are too quiet around here now, anyway."

"Oh no," I said, "I'll stay with you. Thanks anyway, Mrs. Mason."

But she didn't give up. "I'll fix a picnic lunch," she said, "and we could eat in their woods."

"No," I told her, and my tone was definite. "I'm going to stay with Daddy."

"I understand, child," she said. "I'll fix sort of a picnic supper for the two of you, anyway."

Daddy left soon after that and I went into the living room and sat in his chair, thinking of how I could get rid of Mrs.

Mason. I could hear her working in the kitchen, humming in a tuneless sort of way.

Pretty soon I smelled bacon frying and I wondered if she were going against what I had said and would try to make me eat her kind of breakfast. But later I found out she had fried it to put in the baked beans she was making for our picnic supper. When I went to the kitchen to get myself a coke, I saw she'd made potato salad. A little bowl of it was on the top refrigerator shelf, decorated with green peppers and pimentos.

I took my coke up to my room, and not long afterward I heard her thump, thumping up the stairs. I wanted desperately to get rid of her that very day. I wanted her to leave with her nephew and take her suitcase and her package and never come back. I wanted to get up the next morning and cook my father's breakfast. I didn't want my father to go to Chicago and leave me alone with a housekeeper.

I set my coke glass down on my dresser, and not knowing what I was going to do, I left my room and started down the hall toward hers. She was standing in the middle of her room, combing her hair. She looked up and smiled at me.

Then, without having to think of what to do, I just started doing it. I limped down the hall toward her. I dragged my foot sideways, scraping it along the shining floor.

The smile stayed on her face a moment. Then she looked sick, as though she couldn't breathe, and I thought she might fall over. Her face looked awful, and when I got to the door of her room, I was glad to turn and limp back down the hall to mine. I got inside and closed the door and put the desk chair under the handle. I was shaking and when I tried to drink some of my coke, I could hardly hold it. I hated the way she had looked at me. I hated what I had had to do. I wished I hadn't had to be so mean. Because it *was* mean. I knew it was mean. And I wanted to be good. I had thought that with my mother dead it would be easy. I threw myself down on my bed, wondering if all the rest of my life people would make me do bad things the way my mother always had.

I hoped my father would stay at the cemetery a long time and Mrs. Mason's nephew would come after her and she wouldn't have a chance to tell my father anything. But she didn't wait for her nephew. In only a few minutes I heard her thumping down the stairs and out the front door. When I looked through my window, I saw her limping up the street to the bus stop, carrying her suitcase and her package. I stayed at the window and watched until I saw the bus come along. I watched her get on. Only then did I feel like going downstairs.

I wondered if she would tell my aunt Helen what I had done and if my father would hear about it. I wondered what I would tell him when he came home.

Chapter 12

✤ ✤ ✤ ✤ ✤ ✤ ✤ ✤ ✤ ✤ ✤ ✤ ✤

I had the feeling that something bad was going to happen to me. I went to the back door and locked the screen and then I locked the front screen too. But that wasn't enough. As hot as it was, I closed both doors and turned the keys in the locks.

I wanted my father to come home and yet I wasn't ready to have him come. I didn't know what I was going to tell him. It was about noon and bright outside, but I turned on the lights in the living room and sat down on the sofa. The picture that I couldn't get out of my mind was Mrs. Mason's smile changing to that horrible stricken look. She was making me feel almost as though I'd killed her. Deliberately I made myself see her standing at the sink, doing my work, taking over, making herself at home. I thought of how my father had planned to go to Chicago and leave me with her. But the picture of her face kept flashing back into my mind.

I got up and finished the housework which Mrs. Mason hadn't had time to do. The more I worked, the better I felt. There was a rightness to my dusting the furniture and running the vacuum. I got the leather cream and started working on the furniture in my father's den. Before long the phone rang and it was Aunt Helen, wanting to know whether or not we had plans for our Sunday dinner. I told her that we didn't and that if my father came back in time, we'd come to eat with her. I liked the idea of getting out of the house.

As I worked, I thought of the possibilities of what I could

tell my father about Mrs. Mason's leaving. At first I thought I might say that her nephew's wife was sick and she had to take care of her. But I was afraid that later, in several days, my father would try to get in touch with her to see if she were coming back. Whatever I told him, it had to be something that would rule out all possibility of his trying to get her back.

Then I thought of telling him that she had said the work was too hard. The trouble with that was that if he got the idea the work was so hard, he wouldn't want me doing it and he'd be looking for another housekeeper right away.

I still hadn't thought of anything when I heard someone at the front door and it was my father. I let him in, reminding myself that long ago I'd learned not to jump into explanations prematurely. It only made people suspicious.

I told him about Aunt Helen's invitation and he said, "All right. What time does she want us?"

"She said around three," I told him. "Would you like to rest a bit first?"

He said, "No, there are some papers I've got to go over."

He went into his den and sat at the desk and I took coffee to him. Then he worked with his papers, and I rubbed cream into the easy chair near the window. I began to feel peaceful and almost happy. It was good for us to be working in the same room together.

Around two o'clock I went upstairs and dressed. My pink sheath was back from the cleaners, and they'd been able to get out the grass strains. I spent a lot of time on my hair and I liked the way I looked when I went downstairs to my father.

Without glancing up from his desk he said, "Is it time to go?"

I said yes, and we went through the living room together. In the hallway he said, "What about Mrs. Mason? Did her nephew pick her up yet?"

"She's gone," I said.

I didn't blame him for not noticing the way I looked. He had a lot on his mind. He still wasn't himself. He was thin and sad and worried. But gradually things would change. Gradually he'd start really looking at me and then some day he'd say, "You look wonderful in that, Dorrie. I swear you get better looking every day," or maybe, in a year or two, he might even say, "Dorrie, do you know that you are absolutely beautiful?"

I climbed into the car beside him and I had so well imagined what he might say sometime that I felt warm and good.

I had been going to Aunt Helen's all of my life and every time I went into her house I had the same feeling. The house was so clean that when you walked in it seemed to be saying, "Look at me; look at me. See how clean I am." The very corners seemed to be talking. My mother used to say, "I think I'm a pretty good housekeeper, but heavens, you could eat off Helen's kitchen floor."

But my aunt wasn't like a lot of unusually good house-keepers. She didn't mind having you get things out all over the floor to play with. When my cousin, Harry, and I were little, we'd make a mess with blocks or cutting things out of the catalogue or playing with the Erector set. But when it was time for me to go home, Aunt Helen would swoop into the room and pick everything up and not get after us at all. I don't think she deserved any great credit for her attitude. I think she loved so much to keep busy that we were doing her a favor to make a little more work for her.

Harry's father had been dead for so long that neither Harry nor I could remember him. My aunt used to say to my father, "Jim, you'll never know how much I appreciate the interest you take in Harry. You're the nearest he's ever had to a father."

She didn't know that my father thought Harry was a cry-baby and a sissy and a weak sister. My father was right. I could always make Harry cry and then I'd see the look my father would give him. "Come on now, Harry," he'd say. "Be a little man. Buck up, son."

Harry couldn't stand to be teased. He and I would be playing on the floor in Aunt Helen's dining room, and in the adjoining room, in plain sight through the big double doors, our parents would be sitting. Sometimes we'd be running Harry's electric train or sometimes we'd be making some kind of an elaborate structure with his Tinker Toys. After a while I'd get tired of playing. I never just said so. I always ended our playing the same way. Under my breath, so that only Harry could hear it, I'd start chanting, "Hairy ape, hairy ape, hairy ape." I'd go on playing quietly and once in a while I'd stop chanting and would say something to Harry like, "How about putting this one here?" or, "You take a turn now, Harry. It's your turn."

I'd smile at him then, and through almost closed lips I'd go on with my almost silent song. He would begin to get red in the face and he'd look as though he were holding his breath. Then he'd explode. He'd start pounding the floor, or he'd knock over whatever we'd been building, or he'd hit me. It always ended with his crying. The adults would come rushing in and my aunt would look worried and she'd say something like, "Harry, Harry, what's gotten into my little boy? This isn't like him at all."

My father would take me on his lap and pat me and hold me close, and on the way home he'd say to my mother, "I tell you, Eleanore, there's something wrong with that child. It isn't natural for a boy to be such a sissy."

My mother would say, "Oh, Jim, he's just a baby. He'll outgrow it."

It didn't bother me that my mother took Harry's side. Sometimes my father would say, "Well, thank God, Dorrie's not like him. Thank God, she's got some starch to her."

Harry was such a fool that he kept coming back for more. I

could always make him think that everything was going to be all right and that we'd have fun together. I could get him to do anything. It didn't surprise me at all when he was fourteen years old and he let that Jenkins boy talk him into taking a joy ride in the Weatherbys' car without permission. That was just like Harry.

One time when Harry and I were in sixth grade my parents and I were at Aunt Helen's house, and she said, "Jim, it's a lot to ask, but I've been wondering if you would do something for Harry."

My father smiled at her and said, "You know I'll do anything I can, Helen."

She said, "Well, there's going to be this Boy Scout father-son camp-out. And you know how sensitive Harry is. You'd think it was his fault he doesn't have a father. I wondered if you could take the time to go on this trip with him."

"When is it?" my father asked.

"Two weeks from this coming weekend. He's got all the equipment. The only thing you'd need is a bedroll. I think I could borrow one from someplace."

My father's voice was more enthusiastic than I'd ever heard it in connection with Harry. He said, "Didn't you know, I'm an old Boy Scout myself? I always loved camping."

He turned to my mother. "Where is that old bedroll of mine, anyway?"

My mother said it was someplace in the basement, and my father started talking about camping and all the fun he'd had when he was in Scouting. Finally he looked at me and said, "I suppose if Dorrie had been a boy, I'd be a Scoutmaster or something now."

I had the feeling that by being a girl I'd made him miss out on a lot of fun.

Harry began to get real important about the camping trip. He said, "Come on and see my camping equipment, Uncle

Jim." My father got up and they went to Harry's room with me following them. Daddy sat on Harry's bed and Harry kept getting things out to show him. He unfastened his hiking bag and took out every single thing that was in it and handed each one to my father to admire. There were pans that fit inside each other and a knife and a flashlight and a piece of wax wrapped in newspaper to start a fire with. Then he started talking about the awards he had earned and he showed my father the work chart he was keeping. My father put his hand on Harry's shoulder and said, "Why, Harry, you're doing just fine, I'm proud of you, son."

When we left that day, my father called out to Harry, "Good-by, old buddy. We'll show them all what real camping is."

On the way home he said to my mother, "You know, Eleanore, I think Harry's beginning to come out of it. He's awfully interested in Scouting. It may be the making of him."

My mother said, "Well, heaven knows Helen tries hard enough. If Harry doesn't turn out all right, it won't be her fault. I'm glad you're going on the trip. It means a lot to them both."

My father said, "I know. It's rough on the boy not to have his father."

When we were home, my father went right down to the basement and hunted up his sleeping bag. He took it out in the back yard and opened it up and hung it on the line to air. Later that afternoon he took a box out of the basement and opened it and looked over some of his old Boy Scout equipment. There was a knife and a ring and an Indian headdress and even a Boy Scout pen. I hadn't known he had these things, but now he was looking excited and happy and he said, "I wonder if Harry has a compass. Maybe he could use this one."

I took his Boy Scout ring and put it on my finger. He laughed and said, "That's about four sizes too big for you, Dorrie. And anyway, I'm afraid you'll never qualify for Boy Scouts."

Several times during the next two weeks Harry telephoned my father and they talked about the camping trip. They were to leave Friday night and come back Sunday afternoon. The Thursday before, Harry and Aunt Helen came over to our house for dinner. I could see that my father was liking Harry better than he ever had. All through dinner they talked about camping and Scouting.

When we had eaten, I said, "Come on out and play, Harry."

Aunt Helen said, "Yes, run along, you two. The first thing you know, the weather will be bad and you'll be stuck inside."

Harry and I went out in the back yard and for a while we just played with our Yo-yos. But I got tired of that and I started climbing the tree by our garage. As usual, Harry didn't look up at me. He was such a sissy about climbing that he couldn't even bear to see someone high above him. I had gone only about half as high as I could when I stopped and hung onto the limb I was leaning against and said, "Look at me, Harry. I bet you can't do this."

Still working his Yo-yo, he said, "I don't want to."

Then I started singing softly, "Harry's afraid. Harry's afraid."

He tried to act as though he couldn't hear me or else he didn't care. He did three straight round-the-worlds and then I changed my song to "Hairy Ape's afraid. Hairy Ape's afraid. The big Boy Scout is afraid. Better join the Girl Scouts, Harry."

All of a sudden he slammed his Yo-yo against the garage and started climbing the tree. He came faster than I thought he could, and it looked as if he'd gotten over being afraid. When he was almost to me, I climbed up higher. He was slowing down and he reached the place where I had been and stopped and hung onto the limb. It was as though he suddenly realized where he was. His face grew pale and he looked out straight ahead of him, afraid to look up or down.

I took my Yo-yo out of my pocket and started working it up

and down. Then I said, "Look, Harry, here goes my Yo-yo," and I dropped it.

That was when he let go and fell to the ground, screaming. It wasn't very far, but his arm was broken and he didn't go on the camping trip and he missed the first week of school too. My parents kept saying what a shame he'd missed the trip. "That boy does need Scouting," my father said. "Any boy worth his salt ought to be able to climb a tree. Why, Dorrie's been climbing that tree for years."

Now my father and I were at my aunt Helen's house. Harry wouldn't be there—he was away at military school. Aunt Helen had fried chicken and made mashed potatoes and gravy. When we sat down at the table, she started the conversation. She was a stickler for controlling the conversation when she was playing hostess and not controlling it when she was a guest.

She said, "Well, Jim, how's Mrs. Mason working out?"

"Fine, fine," my father said. "She's quite pleasant to have around. She's crazy about Dorrie."

My aunt looked fondly at me and said, "That's not surprising at all. Everyone likes our Dorrie."

Then lowering her voice a little and almost coaxing me by the tone of it to answer yes, she said, "Do you like her, honey?"

"She's all right," I said.

Aunt Helen put a spoon in the strawberry preserves and handed them to my father. "Well, that's settled. I *was* worried at the thought of you two there alone with no one to look after you. Mrs. Berkson's known Mrs. Mason for years. Everyone says she's a fine woman."

She looked at me then and went on. "And I did understand your feelings, Dorrie. I know how you felt. But no one's trying to take your mother's place. No one could."

She looked down at the table and her face was stiff as if she were trying to keep from crying. But she got herself under control and said, "Jim, I've been thinking. Eleanore had so many friends. I've been wondering if we could go through the pictures we have of her and pick out one to give to them. So many people would treasure a picture of her."

"Why, yes, Helen, I like that idea," my father said. "We could have copies made and send them to people. I've got some wonderful pictures of her."

Aunt Helen said, "I know. She was always herself, even when her picture was being taken, and her aliveness came through in them."

My aunt cleared the table and brought sherbet and almond cookies. "If you like," she said, "I'll come over tomorrow night and help you choose a picture."

"Fine," my father said. Then he said to me, "Dorrie, do you suppose that tomorrow you could go through things and get all the pictures together?"

I told him I would. Later he went into the living room and sat holding a magazine on his lap, but I could tell he wasn't reading it. I helped Aunt Helen with the dishes. When we finished, she motioned to a chair at the kitchen table and said, "Sit down a moment, Dorrie. There's something I have to talk to you about."

She spoke in a low voice so my father wouldn't hear. "Dorrie," she said, "you said something the other day that cut me to the quick. You said that Eleanore criticized my care of Harry —that I was such a busybody that I neglected him. Now, honey, I know you were upset and angry, and sometimes we say things we don't mean."

She stopped, and I knew she was hoping desperately that I would say I'd lied.

She said, "I want you to tell me the truth now. Did your mother really say that?"

I didn't hesitate. I looked her straight in the eyes and said, "Yes, Aunt. I heard her say it many times."

She bit her lip and looked down at the floor and I felt sorry for her. But I knew what would happen if I told the truth. She would forgive me and be loving, and the whole thing would strengthen her and weaken me. I'd learned long ago to protect myself from people. If you let them know too much about you, they moved in on you. There was special danger from someone with a strong personality like my aunt's. The whole incident was her fault, anyway. If she hadn't pushed so hard at the housekeeper idea, she wouldn't have driven me to tell the lie.

On the way home that evening my father and I stopped for a while at my grandma's. Because she wasn't feeling well, she hadn't been able to come to my aunt's dinner. We took her some chicken and cookies, but she wasn't hungry and I put them in the kitchen.

It was almost dark when we got home. There were no lights on in the house and my father said, "Well, Mrs. Mason's making a day of it. I'm glad she is. The poor thing deserves some pleasure."

That night I had one of those quick dreams that are like snapshots. I saw Mrs. Mason shaking her fist at me. I woke up wishing that she really had. It would have been better to remember that than to remember the awful look I'd seen on her face.

Chapter 13

The next morning I made coffee and took it to my father's room.

"Daddy," I said, "Mrs. Mason's gone. I looked in her room and she's taken her things. Everything's gone."

My father looked astonished. He set the cup down on the bedside table and went to her room.

"Why, I can hardly believe it," he said. "She must have known yesterday she wasn't coming back. Did you see her leave?"

I looked out the window and said, "No, I must have been taking a bath. When I got dressed, she wasn't here. Of course I didn't look in her room until this morning when she wasn't downstairs."

"I wonder what got into her," he said. "Did anything happen yesterday morning? Did she say anything?"

"No, nothing unusual."

He walked back down the hall to his room. "I would have sworn she liked it here," he said. "She didn't seem like the kind of person who would just up and go without saying anything."

"Well, of course, we really didn't know her very well," I said.

"No, but she didn't seem like the flighty sort. Helen said she had excellent recommendations. I just don't understand."

I went downstairs and made pancakes for my father, but his appetite still wasn't good and I had to throw away more than half the batter. When he had gone to the office, I made my list of housekeeping chores and wrote out my menu for dinner. At ten o'clock I called my father's office. "Daddy," I said, "Mrs. Mason just phoned."

"Well, what did she have to say?" he asked.

"She said she doesn't like this location—it's too far from her nephew's house. She's going to take a job on the other side of town."

My father sighed. "It seems she would have thought of that in the beginning," he said. "Well, don't worry about it, baby. I know you were fond of her, but things will work out."

When I finished doing my housework, I started collecting my mother's pictures. In order to get more compliments on her looks she used to say, "I'm so photogenic it's embarrassing. I'm not half so good-looking as my pictures come out." And then whoever was listening would say, "Why, Eleanore, that just isn't true. Some of these pictures don't even do you justice."

My mother was a good-looking woman but not the raving beauty the family thought. Because she was so much better looking than my aunt, people thought she was beautiful. There was something about the way she acted, too, that fooled people into thinking so.

She never wanted me to be good-looking. In fifth grade, when some of the girls started wearing lipstick and I wanted to, she said, "Heavens, no, Dorie. You're still a little girl. You'll grow up fast enough as it is."

But I went into the dime store and bought some lipstick and for a while I put it on every day on my way to school and washed it off in the girl's room every evening before I went home. I looked much prettier with it than I did without it. But it didn't seem worth the trouble just to wear it around the kids. And my mother never wanted my father to think I was pretty.

She proved that when I was May queen. I was in sixth grade

then, and I went to the beauty shop and they made shining curls all over my head. I had a long white dress, with little pink rosebuds sewn on the skirt, and on my hair I wore a crown that looked just like a queen's. When my mother finished helping me dress, she went into her bedroom, and I knew my father was downstairs so I went down the stairway slowly and gracefully as a queen would. When I went into the living room, my father looked up from his newspaper and said, "Is this little Dorrie Lawson? Why, it can't be. This is a beautiful queen from a foreign land who has wandered into our living room by mistake."

I could tell he was going to go on and on, and he would have, too, but my mother came in and put a stop to it. She had on a new green sheath and my father looked at her and whistled and said, "Good Lord, Eleanore, I don't know if I want you to go out in that or not—all the fellows will be falling for you."

He jumped up and grabbed her and danced around the room with her. They were both happy and laughing, and my father didn't say anything more about the way I looked.

People always said my parents made a handsome couple, and there were lots of pictures of them together. Once, when I was much younger, I had a snapshot of them and my mother caught me cutting her picture out of it. A strange look came over her face and she said, "Dorrie, Dorrie, what are you doing that for?"

"I want a picture just of Daddy," I said.

She was silent for a moment and then she said, "Well, all right. But no more cutting pictures. We just don't do that."

Then she hunted around until she found me a picture of my father. I kept it under the glass on my dressing table and when I was older and had a billfold I put it there.

I took a box from the basement and put the pictures and the albums in it. There were all kinds of pictures of my mother—photographs, snapshots, pictures of her all dressed up, and pictures of her in shorts and swimming suits. When I saw the ones we'd taken at the lake, it made me think of the accident. If anyone was to blame for the accident, it wasn't me. Anyone can get a headache.

Aunt Helen was late getting to our house to go over the pictures that night because Grandma still wasn't feeling well. It reminded me of how happy I'd been the last time Grandma was sick and my mother had to go and stay with her evenings. When I'd get home from school, my mother would tell me what she had ready for dinner and how to set the table, as though I didn't know, and to be sure to wash the dishes, and then she'd kiss me and say, "Be good now, honey," and she'd wade out through the snow to her taxi. I'd watch it drive off and I'd feel as though the house were mine, and when my father came home, he'd be mine, and there would be that lovely feeling that my mother didn't exist.

I didn't wish my grandma any harm, but I'd never cared for her particularly, and it would have been all right with me if she'd never gotten well. Not that I wanted her to die, but I just to go on being sick and needing my mother and leaving me to take care of my father. The only trouble was that every night, after my mother got Grandma settled, she came back home to sleep.

One particular night my mother was off to a late start because it was snowing hard and taxis were running behind. But finally she was gone and I kept busy getting ready for my father to come home. I did all of the usual things, setting the table, checking the casserole, and then I had this wonderful idea. I'd never made divinity, but I'd watched my mother, and I decided that just because she was gone was no reason my father shouldn't have some. My father was always saying, "Eleanore, you make the best divinity in the world."

I took out the cookbook and read and reread the recipe. I decided not to make it until after supper and then he'd know

I'd done it alone with no help from her. But I did set out the things I'd need—the nuts, the eggs, the sugar, the vanilla. I took the cover off the Mixmaster and got out the double boiler. I had just finished when the phone rang and it was my mother, calling from my grandma's neighbor's house, saying Grandma was much better and she could stay alone. My mother had tried to get a taxi, but now they were running hours behind because of the snow, but with Daddy's new snow tires he wouldn't have any trouble. If I'd just turn off the oven and open the door, the casserole would keep, and when Daddy got home, we could come after her and we'd all get to eat together. That was typical of the way she always ruined things for me.

I felt just sick and I said, "Yes, Mother, I'll tell him," and I hung up.

When Daddy came home, I decided to let him have his drink and read the paper and rest a bit before I told him. There was no need to rush right out. While he was mixing his drink, he looked up at me and said, "Dorrie, be a good girl and call Ed Mayhew and tell him I won't be able to make the meeting tonight."

When I tried to use the phone, it was dead, because of the storm, and the first thing I thought of was that no one could call us and especially my mother.

Right then I knew I wasn't going to give him the message. The evening slipped by from his reading his paper to eating dinner, and then I made the divinity. When I was finished and had put some in a nice pattern on the pansy plate, he tasted it and said, "Well, this is a surprise. I didn't know you could make divinity. I never tasted better." This made me so happy that I didn't even say thank you to him. I wasn't a bit sorry about my mother. She could sleep at Grandma's for once. I had a right to some time with my father.

At nine o'clock Daddy sent me upstairs to bed, and I had

just finished my shower and was putting on my pajamas when I heard the front doorbell and it was my mother. She just didn't give up. She'd decided we couldn't get the car started and had finally caught a taxi. Of course it all came out about the message I'd forgotten to give Daddy, and I could hear him say, "I don't know what ails that child. She's got to learn to take some responsibility."

My mother said, "It *is* exasperating. But I remember how I was at her age. Kind of dreamy and out of touch."

My father said, "You're too easy on her, Eleanore. She's got to be taught."

My mother was satisfied then, because she'd given him the impression she was so tolerant, and she said, "We'll mention it to her in the morning. Right now I'd like some hot chocolate. What about you?"

They went on out to the kitchen and I couldn't hear any more, but I knew Daddy was telling her about what happened at the office or what he'd heard at the barbershop that day. She always acted so interested that he never bothered telling me anything.

Almost as soon as Aunt Helen was in the door that night, my father told her about Mrs. Mason. My aunt had started to put her purse on the hall table, but she stopped in mid-air and said, "Why, I can hardly believe it! I ran into Mrs. Berkson today and she was telling me Mrs. Mason loved it here."

"Well, anyway, she's gone," my father said. "She wanted to be nearer her nephew's. She didn't even mention it before she left. Just called Dorrie this morning."

I didn't like the way my aunt looked at me. "Did anything happen, Dorrie," she asked, "anything you're not telling?"

I looked her square in the eye. "Why, no, Aunt," I said. "She wanted me to go to her nephew's with her and I didn't want to, but that's all."

"You didn't say anything to her? You didn't let her know you didn't want a housekeeper?"

"Aunt," I said, "I brought her coffee and gave her cokes and put flowers in her room."

"Dorrie made every effort," my father said. "They were getting along fine. No, Mrs. Mason was just unpredictable, that's all."

My aunt looked at my father. "All right, all right," she said. She turned to me then and said, "But you always have been a strong-willed child."

That was just about the end of that affair. A month later I heard my aunt telling my father that she'd seen Mrs. Mason and asked her why she left. She said Mrs. Mason was vague, just said she had thought it was for the best.

Going through my mother's pictures was pretty boring, but my father wanted me to help, so I did. They finally picked out a photograph taken about a year ago when she was head of the United Fund campaign.

Before she left that night, my aunt said, "Now, let's see," and she ticked off her plans on her fingers. "I'll get copies made of this. I'll come over some day soon and start going through Eleanore's things." She sighed then and looked at me. "And I'll be on the lookout for a new housekeeper."

My father's voice was weary. "All right, Helen," he said. "Whatever you think."

She wasn't going to give up. She was as stubborn as my mother. I stood at the front door and watched her go to her car, and as she tried to start the motor a bomb under the hood exploded and there was never any trace again of her or her car.

I went back to the living room and asked my father if he'd like something to eat before bedtime, but he said, "No, I'm not hungry. You eat something. I'll be back later."

I knew where he was going and the look on his face hurt me.

I wanted to comfort him. I wanted to hold his head against my shoulder and put my arms around him and rock him. There was nothing at the cemetery to comfort him. There was only a hill and some trees and some dying strips of sod. No one was there.

Chapter 14

❧ ❧ ❧ ❧ ❧ ❧ ❧ ❧ ❧ ❧ ❧ ❧

The days went by and my father and I were allowed to settle down to a comfortable routine. My grandma got worse and Aunt Helen's time was taken up with her. My father canceled his plans to go to Chicago with the Stevensons. Mrs. Berkson came over several times—I suspected so she could report to Aunt Helen. Mainly our days were filled with Daddy's going to the office and my keeping house for him.

Daddy still went to the cemetery every night and he didn't eat much and he looked sad and tired. But I reminded myself that I had a lifetime ahead of me to make him happy. I was a little worried because he was drinking more than he ever had before. I don't mean he was an alcoholic, but he drank faster and longer than was good for him. Before my mother died, drinking made him more talkative. Now it only made him more silent.

Sandy called me every day to see if I had found the key, and every day I had to say no. When finally I did, it was by accident. It was on a Sunday afternoon and my father had gone to the cemetery. It was a hot, glaring day with not a breeze stirring, and yet there was in the air the feeling of a storm coming. It was so quiet that I could hear the rustle of the cottonwood in the back yard. I had taken a book and gone into my father's den to read. I was sitting in his chair when I noticed a cobweb on the frame of his diploma. I was disgusted with myself for not noticing it when I cleaned his room and I got the dustcloth and took the frame off the wall. The key was hanging on the nail behind.

I forgot the diploma. I didn't even hang it back up. I laid it on the desk and ran up the stairs two at a time. I hadn't doubted that the key would fit and I was right. I slipped it into the lock; it turned, and I could hardly breathe with excitement.

In the drawer there were newspaper clippings and a long white envelope. From one of the clippings my father's face leaped out at me. I started to read the print below.

> James Lawson of 489 Maple Street,
> an adjuster for Lifeline Guarantee
> Company, was indicted today on a
> charge of conspiring to defraud.

I looked again at the picture of my father. He was younger then, much younger. And I had been younger too. From the dates on the clippings I knew it had happened the summer I was in third grade. It was beginning to come back. My mother crying. My father away. The house on Maple Street darker and drearier than ever. And then my mother saying to me, "Your grandma's lonesome. She wants you to come stay with her a while."

Then there were the endless summer months at my grandmother's house. My mother visited me sometimes, saying, "Daddy's busy. He sends you his love. Here's a kiss from him." But I didn't want my mother delivering kisses from my father. I wanted my father.

There were the long dull days at Grandma's, listening to her rules and trying to remember them. "No, Sister, you can't go out now. The noonday sun is too hot. You'd get sunstroke." "Chew each mouthful thirty times. That's a big girl. That way you'll get the good of your food." "Ladies don't cross their legs. Sit like Grandma does."

The days were without end. At noon I sometimes thought it

was time for the evening meal and for the sun to go down. I couldn't believe I'd only made it through half a day. I longed to see my father and I'd plan to run away to my own house across town, but I only planned. I never did it. In the mornings my grandma would say, "You sit here now, Sister, and do your memory work." And I would sit memorizing sections of the Bible and hating every word of it. In the afternoons I had to do embroidery. Grandma taught me how to make French knots and cross-stitch, and if I didn't do it right, I had to rip it out and start over again.

In the late afternoon Grandma and I would take our baths and then sit out on her front porch and she would call hello to people who went by. All of them were old and dull like her. The period of sitting on the porch was as dull as the rest of the day.

Even the food at Grandma's was dull. Once I said, "Grandma, I'm tired of chicken soup," and she said, "That's all right, Sister. This is rabbit soup." But I knew it wasn't and I knew that she wouldn't count what she said a lie. But it was a lie and it was a lie that said, "You're young. I can tell you anything. I can fool you."

I finally got to go back to live at my own house and see my father again. But now, sitting on the bed holding the clippings, I remembered something else which I hadn't thought of for years. Johnny Blake said something to me; what it was had slipped away. But I could remember yelling, "You're a liar. My father is not either a crook." And then I started pounding Johnny and it didn't make any difference that he was already a head taller than I. He cringed against the garage until someone came out and pulled me away from him.

I never liked Johnny again, but not until that day on the bed in my father's room did I remember why.

There were several other clippings, about the trial and about my father making restitution and getting a suspended sentence.

In the envelope there was a sheet of paper which was a record of a loan my aunt had made to my father. She had given him ten thousand dollars.

I wadded the clippings up in my fists and I pounded the bed and I was crying. They'd tried to crucify him. And I had been put out of the way so I couldn't be a comfort to him. I hadn't even been allowed to know about it. That had been my mother's doing.

And she was the one who had kept the clippings all those years. What had made her want to keep these lies about my father? And then I knew. She'd wanted me to find them. When it was too late for me to help him through his hard time, then she wanted me to know about it. It was one more attempt to separate my father and me.

I stopped crying and slipped the white paper back into its envelope. Then I put it in the dresser drawer and locked it. I took the wads of clippings downstairs, got matches from the kitchen, and went out to the incinerator. I stood in the heat of the sun and watched the clippings turn black and crinkle and burn until no one could have told what they were. I took a stick and stirred and stirred them into the ashes.

In my father's den I replaced the key on the nail and hung his diploma over it. I dialed Sandy's number and let it ring twice and hung up. In a short time I heard her tapping at the back screen door. We went up to my room and I turned on the radio in case my father should come back. I couldn't bear to have him hear what I was saying and be reminded of the terrible thing that had been done to him.

Sandy agreed with me completely as to why my mother had kept the clippings. Sandy wasn't good at schoolwork, but she was a lot smarter than people gave her credit for.

Sandy had fifty cents with her and she wanted me to walk down to the drugstore for a soda, but I told her I wanted to be there when my father came home. I gave her a coke and when she had drunk it, I said, "Well, I'll see you," and she said, "See you," and left.

The hot stillness of the afternoon was beginning to change into more definite signs of a storm. In the west there were big rolling black clouds, and the wind was sending swirls of dust up the street. I saw Mrs. Berkson run out and fold her lawn chairs and take them into the house. Already I could smell rain, although it hadn't yet started falling. When it did, it pounded down in huge sheets and soon all the sky was dark. It came straight down and I needn't have closed the windows, but I did anyway. Having them closed made me feel safer. Ever since Mrs. Mason had left, I'd had periods of being afraid.

I turned on all the lights and wished my father would come home. Surely he wouldn't stay at the cemetery in such a storm. It would be terribly dangerous on that hill if there were lightning. I sat on the sofa in the living room and looked out into the street, watching for him to come. Cars crept by, their lights hardly picking a way through the heavy rain. Finally one came to a stop halfway between our house and the Springers' next door. After a few minutes someone got out of the car and came running up our front walk and rang the doorbell. It was a man whose car had stalled and who needed to use our phone. He followed me into the living room and I pointed to my father's den. It took him only a minute to call someone and he thanked me and ran back to his car. But as luck would have it, during the short time he'd used the phone, Aunt Helen had been trying to call me.

"Your line was busy," she said, when she'd reached me. "Were you talking?"

"No, Aunt," I said. "Someone with car trouble needed the phone. It took him only a minute."

She sounded excited and she said, "Your father's here at my

house. Are you there alone? Did you let a strange man into the house?"

"Aunt," I said, "he was a perfectly ordinary man who had car trouble. He used the phone and went out. That's all there was to it."

"Dorrie," she said, "that's dangerous. You just can't do things like that. You've got to use your head."

"All right," I told her, "I won't do it again."

But the damage was already done. It set her off on how much we needed someone there to take care of my father and me. She told my father it wasn't right for me to be left alone and that when school started, I couldn't be coming home to an empty house. The fact that I hadn't been the least bit afraid of the man meant nothing to her. Actually, the few minutes he'd been in the house, I'd felt better. The fear I'd felt earlier had something to do with Mrs. Mason, and I knew it didn't make sense. She'd had a chance to tell on me, and she hadn't done it. I told myself many times that she wouldn't harm me. But every so often I'd think I heard a thumping on the stairs.

Now my aunt turned her attention to getting us another housekeeper. I hated to see the way she was running my father, telling him what to do. But my mother had done the same thing and he was used to it. When I was little, my mother would say, "Daddy wants you to be a big girl and eat all your mashed potatoes."

My father would smile and say, "That's right, baby. Eat your potatoes." When I was older, I knew that she was the one who wanted me to eat. She was running things.

This time it took my aunt a week to find someone. My father had gone to work and I was just wiping the kitchen table when I heard my aunt at the front door. Her shrill voice cut right through me. "Dorrie, Dorrie," she called as she came into the house.

"Yes, Aunt," I said. "I'm here, in the kitchen."

After she had shown how much at home she was in my kitchen by helping herself to coffee, she sat down at the table and began her speech.

"I've found someone, Dorrie," she said. "This is someone I know you'll like. She's a good deal younger than Mrs. Mason —about thirty, I'd say. Her name's Anna Chamberlain and she's kept house for years for her father and brother."

"What will they do without her?" I asked.

"Her father died last spring and her brother's married now. She wants to move into town. They live over near Burlington."

And now my aunt's voice changed, softened a little, as though she wanted to show she wasn't scolding me. Sometimes it seemed to me she must hear in her mind directions on how to speak, the way you find them in a play.

She said, "Dorrie, I've always thought there was something funny about Mrs. Mason's leaving, although she wouldn't say a word when I asked her. I know how dead set you've been against having someone come in."

She reached across the table and covered my hand with hers —and again I could see the stage directions telling her to do this.

"Now I'm not accusing you of anything," she went on, "but I want you to examine your conscience. You know what I'm doing is for the best, for your own good. And Jim agrees completely. I want you to decide you're going to get along with this new girl."

"Aunt," I said, "I couldn't very well lock Mrs. Mason in her room to keep her from leaving. Could I do that? Is that what you expected of me?"

"Dorrie," she said, "anyone can be sarcastic. It isn't at all becoming."

She stood up and rinsed her cup and put it in the dishwasher.

Then she let out one of her long sighs and said, "Well, all I can say is that I hope to goodness this works out. I won't rest easy until you're settled with someone to look after you."

Sometimes I wonder now if my aunt ever thinks of that day.

Chapter 15

That night when my father came home from work, I had my hair fixed a new way. He hadn't noticed the French roll and I was tired of it. That afternoon I washed my hair and then sat in the sun and brushed it dry, I went into my father's bathroom and made a part in front and combed my hair down over my face. Then, being very careful to get them straight, I cut bangs across my forehead. My hair was parted in the middle and fell smooth and shining on either side of my face. As I dressed, I warned myself that he might not notice the change right away.

He came home a little early, and I was just carrying the tray into the living room when he walked in the front door. He didn't notice my hair. He said, "Hello, baby," and started fixing his drink.

I had decided it was time for me to stop referring to my mother's sister as aunt. I was a little too old for that. I said, "Helen was here this morning."

My father sipped his scotch. "Yes, I know," he said. "She called me. It seems I'm to go out this afternoon to pick up this new woman."

My aunt wasn't wasting any time. I said, "Dinner's ready now. Do you want to eat early?"

He said, "No, I'm not hungry. I might as well go when I finish my drink."

He finished that drink, and another, and then he pushed himself out of the chair and said, "I guess I'll get started."

I waited until he was at the front door. Then I said, "Do you want me to go with you?"

"If you like," he called back, and I followed him out to the car.

We drove to the edge of town and on out the highway toward Burlington. I knew we would go past the cemetery and I held my breath, hoping he wouldn't stop. He didn't and then I wished he had. It would have kept him from making his later visit there.

For half an hour we drove along the highway. I started several conversations. I'd developed the habit during the day, when I was doing my housework, of jotting down interesting things to say. While I dressed in the afternoons, I kept the list on my bureau, glancing at it from time to time until I had it memorized.

I said, "Daddy, what do you think about the mayor's proposal for redistricting?"

My father held his cigar out the window, letting the ashes blow off, and said, "I don't know, baby. I'm sure I don't know."

That had been the last item on my list and I sat beside him wracking my mind, trying to think of something really interesting.

Shortly before we would have reached Burlington, my father turned down a narrow dirt road and we went along it for a mile or two. On either side there were poor, scraggly-looking cornfields. Finally the road veered to the right and there before us was a small farmhouse, poorer looking than the fields had been.

We drove into the yard between the house and the barn, and even the dog that came barking at us looked skinny and poor. A man appeared around the side of a shed and waved a hammer he happened to have in his hand and came up and said, "Howdy."

My father held out his hand. "My name's Lawson," he said. "Does Anna Chamberlain live here?"

"My sister," the man said. "Come on in."

I had never seen such a bare room. There was a platform rocker and a sofa and a straight chair. Under the window by the front door was a small table with some kind of plant in a Folger's coffee can. The wallpaper was a faded brown, and the only picture was a gaudy colored one of Jesus which hung over the sofa. The floor was covered with linoleum with a path worn clear through it from the front door into the kitchen. There wasn't a book or a magazine or a television set or a radio, and I wondered what on earth these people did in their spare time for amusement.

A woman came out of the kitchen, wiping her hands on her apron.

"The wife," the man said, and she nodded to us and said, "Make yourselves to home. I'll call Annie. She's all packed."

She disappeared into the kitchen and then let out a yell that could have been heard a block away. "Annie, Annie," she called.

Still holding the hammer, the man leaned against the front door. "Probably off looking at birds," he said. "I never seen the like."

There was silence then for a few minutes and I sat waiting to see what kind of a person this Anna Chamberlain would be. If she resembled her brother, she certainly wouldn't be good-looking.

There was a sound in the kitchen and the woman we'd met said, "Where you been? Don't you know they're waiting?"

Anna wasn't anything like her brother, but she wasn't good-looking either. She was one of those women who don't want to be. She came into the living room and my father stood up and said, "I'm Jim Lawson. This is my daughter, Dorrie."

She half smiled and said hello and then stood there waiting to be told what to do.

"Well, get a move on," her brother said. "The man ain't got all day."

Anna moved into the adjoining front room and came back carrying a cheap suitcase.

My father took it from her and said, "Well, I guess we'll be going."

He nodded to the woman standing in the kitchen doorway and said, "It's nice to have met you."

She said, "Same here," and then as though she'd just thought of it, she said, "Wait, Annie, I've got something for you."

When she came back into the room, she was carrying a red plastic purse. "You admired it so," she said, "you can have it." Anna smiled then, a real smile, and I saw how pretty she could be if she tried.

"Oh, thank you, Effie," she said and went to the older woman and gave her a hug. That was when I knew they were tickled to death to get rid of Anna. The woman held herself stiff, not wanting the hug, wanting only to be rid of her sister-in-law. The purse wasn't a going-away present. It was a thank-you-for-leaving-us present. I could see plainly that Anna was the outsider.

Going home, we hardly talked at all. Anna sat in the back seat. It reminded me of the times when my mother and father and I were going some place in the car and my mother would say to me, "Come sit in front with us, Dorrie, the three musketeers in the front seat."

But I knew I wasn't welcome in the front seat between them. I always rode in the back by myself. But now it wasn't I who sat there.

When we were home, my father carried Anna's suitcase to the

room at the head of the stairs. I wondered how many women we'd have to give the room to before my aunt got it through her head that we weren't going to have a housekeeper. I promised myself that in less than a week Anna would be gone.

I called up the stairs and said, "Dinner's ready, Anna. Do you want to unpack later?"

She came down and into the kitchen to help me, but she was only in my way. All I had to do was make the iced tea and put the food on the table. I asked her to put ice in the glasses, but I had to show her how to get the cubes out of the tray. When the tea had steeped, I poured it into the pitcher. I wanted to carry the roast in myself, so I handed the pitcher to her. When she took it from me, I could see that her hands were shaking. I glanced at her face and saw that she was almost sick with nervousness. I felt like yelling, "Boo!" This one was going to be easy to get rid of.

During dinner my father tried to be polite to her.

"Have you always lived near Burlington?" he asked.

"Yes," she said, not looking up from her plate.

"I understand there used to be coal mining around there," he said.

She didn't answer. She had no conception of how to keep a conversation going.

As we ate, I could see the three of us sitting there at the table, myself as clearly as the other two. I saw my father with the tired lines in his face. And I saw Anna, colorless, scared, unsure of herself. And I saw me, with my shining brown hair and my bangs and my pale-green dress. I was getting prettier every day. Every day I was older, not just by a day, but growing older by leaps and bounds. I saw my good table manners and the graceful way I held myself. I saw that I was becoming worthy of my father.

I don't know where I was while I looked at myself. The psychologist never explained it. All he had was smart-aleck remarks. The first time I was in his office he said, "What seems to be the trouble, Dorrie?"

I said, "So far as I know, there is no trouble."

He twisted around in his chair and said, "That's not what your mother says."

I said, "If my mother has trouble, let her come to see you."

He put a patient look on his face and said, "Now, Dorrie, I think you're a bright enough girl to know why you're here."

I didn't say anything then, and neither did he for a long time. I had never known before how hard it was to sit in a room with someone, not reading, not doing anything, just sitting and not saying one single word. He was good at it. He used it like a weapon. Later I was on to him, but that first time I finally gave in and I said, "May I go now?"

"I think we have a problem to work on," he said.

I said, "I don't know what my mother has to complain about. I'm making straight A's."

"Did it ever occur to you, Dorrie," he asked, "that making straight A's might not be the answer to everything? Maybe getting along with people is important too."

"You mean that silly class project," I said.

"That's just what I mean," he said, and I saw I'd done exactly what he wanted me to do. He always liked to feel he'd led you into saying a certain thing.

He started fooling around with his pipe, and when he had it going, he leaned back in his chair and in a very phony paternal tone of voice he said, "Now tell me about that silly class project."

I knew he'd already heard about it from my mother, but I didn't want to stay there the rest of my life so I told him what had happened. I spoke slowly and distinctly in the most irritating way I knew.

"Joe Gillespie was assigned to be my partner and I just simply didn't want him for a partner," I said. "I don't like him. I have never liked him."

"What's so bad about Joe Gillespie? I understand he's pretty popular around school."

"Anyone can be popular," I said. "All you have to do is smile at people in the hall."

"You sound bitter, Dorrie," he said. "Could it be you'd like to be popular like Joe?"

I smiled at him. "That's about as stupid a guess as I ever heard," I said. "Nothing could be less important to me than being popular."

"You don't like to be liked?" He was working with his pipe again.

"Please, Dr. Endicott," I said, "I'd like to be going home. My father will be looking for me."

"I understand something about your father came into this," he said.

"Yes," I said, cutting off my words, "something about my father did come into it. But that was a long time ago and doesn't have anything to do with my mother's idiotic idea to send me here."

He was a master at keeping his voice kind and patient. He had his face under control, too, and the look he gave me came close to being loving.

In his oily voice he said, "Tell me what it was about your father, Dorrie."

I thought I'd keep still and not say one other word to him, but pretty soon I doubled up my fists and I said, "All right, Dr. Endicott, I'll tell you."

Then I told him about the time almost a year before that, when my mother made me accept a date with Joe Gillespie. I told him about going to the school dance and doing all the stupid things I was supposed to do. I told him about dancing with every dull, pimply boy who asked me. And finally, going to the drive-in afterward for hamburgers with Joe. And then when we got to my house, Joe saying, "God damn it, Dorrie, the way you talk about your father all the time you'd think he was Jesus H. Christ. Don't you ever think about anything else?"

And then that smart-aleck Dr. Endicott said to me, "Do you?"

I got up and marched out of his office and so far as I was concerned I was through with him, but my parents had this report about what happened when Joe and I were assigned to work on the geometry report together and I stuck my compass into his hand, and they made me go back. Actually it barely nicked him, but from the way the teacher acted, you'd have thought I'd committed murder. I wouldn't have done it at all if it hadn't been for what Joe said.

We were over in a corner of the classroom, trying to make plans for the project, when Joe said to me, "How about going to a movie Friday night?"

I said, "I thought you didn't care for my conversation."

He said, "Aw, come off it, Dorrie. You going to hold one little remark against me the rest of my life? Anyway, you did talk about your old man an awful lot."

"It just happens," I said, "that I might do it again. I wouldn't want to bore you, but I am proud of him. Of course, I have a right to be. Not everyone can be proud of his father."

Everyone in school knew Joe's father was a no-good bum alcoholic and he knew that I knew it. His face got red and he didn't look at all like the good fellow the kids thought he was.

He said, "That's dirty. That's just plain dirty." He stood up then and looked down at me, one hand resting on the table. "All right, Miss High and Mighty," he said. "It'll be a cool day in hell before I ask you for a date again. But let me tell you this: from what I hear, you don't know your old man at all. Not at all, girlie. He's pulled some pretty low stuff in this town."

I stuck my compass into his hand, not half as far as I should have. And everyone got excited, and even the teachers that I thought liked me said, yes, for years we've known she's anti-social.

After that first session with Dr. Endicott I learned how not to talk when I was in there, and it wasn't long before he told my mother I wasn't co-operating and he was afraid I wasn't a good subject for therapy. That suited me fine.

Now I stopped standing off somewhere and watching Anna and my father and me and we had finished our meal and it was time for dessert.

Anna said, "Shall I get the pie?"

I said, "Yes, Anna, please do."

She brought the pie plates in and slopped them down on our plates, on top of the leftover gravy and vegetables and anything else we hadn't eaten.

When she went to the kitchen the second time to get her own pie, my father looked at me from the end of the table and I'll never forget that look. He frowned, and yet he was amused, and he was sending me a secret, private message. His look said, "You and I know that this isn't the proper way to serve dessert."

Suddenly I was happier than I'd been since my mother died. My father and I were in something together. It wasn't the bubble, but it was something. Anna was on the outside.

Then it hit me. In order for me to be on the inside of the bubble with my father, someone had to be on the outside. And she was it. I wasn't going to get rid of her. I was going to keep her.

Chapter 16

When we had finished eating our apple pie, Anna cleared the table and I followed my father into the living room. He picked up the cigar I'd laid out for him and started lighting it. When he had it going, he looked across at me and in a low voice said, "I swear, Dorrie, you've got a job on your hands."

"What do you mean, Daddy?" I asked him.

"Her." He pointed his cigar in the direction of the kitchen. "You're going to have to teach her. I think she's willing enough, but she's not used to our ways. Do you think you can show her how we do things, give her some direction?"

"Of course I can, Daddy. Why, I don't suppose she even knows how to use the dishwasher." I stood up. "Don't worry, I'll take care of things."

As I walked to the kitchen I could see that I was going to be the lady of the house in a way my mother never had been. My mother had done almost all of her own work. I would not do any of the heavy work. I would do the planning, the directing. I would do the things which took a light, delicate touch. I would cut the bouquets and arrange the flowers. I would cook my father's favorite foods. I would get his scotch and his cigar and his paper ready for him. And I would see to it that Anna did her work well. I would teach her.

Anna was standing at the counter, scraping garbage onto a paper.

I made my voice low and kind. "I'll show you how to do things tonight," I said.

She said, "Thank you, Dorrie. I've never worked for anyone before."

I dumped the garbage off the paper into the sink and showed her how to use the garbage disposal. She was delighted with it. "That's a wonderful help," she said. "It must save a lot of time."

I showed her how to place the dishes in the dishwasher and how much powder to use and how to turn it on.

"And every night before you leave the kitchen, the dishes are to be put away in the cupboard," I said. My mother had been in the habit of leaving them in the dishwasher until morning.

She said, "Yes, of course," and it struck me that her way of speaking was nothing like that of her brother or his wife. She was over most of the nervousness she'd shown before dinner, but still her voice was soft and quiet.

When the dishwasher had turned itself off, I helped her put the dishes away. "This is my best china and crystal," I said, "and I'm particular with it. We use it every evening for dinner. At lunch, when my father isn't here, we use the everyday dishes."

I liked the way she handled my china. Her movements were gentle and yet efficient. And I liked the way she accepted me completely as her mistress. I felt as though I were the heroine in a novel. I could hear my father saying to the Stevensons some evening, "Anna didn't know how to do things when she came, but Dorrie took her in hand and now this house is running like clockwork. Dorrie's a marvelous manager."

"Anna," I said when we had finished in the kitchen, "why don't you go up and unpack and get settled and then come to my room? It's down the hall on the north. I'd like to get you straightened out for tomorrow."

"All right, Dorrie," she said, and I could see she'd been bossed all of her life. She was twice my age and yet she was eager to have me tell her what to do. And she was used to being on the outside too. She'd accepted it as I never had. She wouldn't be trying to come between my father and me. Being on the outside had weakened her, made her passive, submissive. It had only strengthened me. I didn't have it in me to give up.

In my room I made notes on what I wanted to remember to tell Anna. When she knocked on my door, I was ready.

I smiled at her. "Come in. Sit here." I motioned to my rocker.

"Now, Anna," I started, "there won't be anything more you need to do tonight. And ordinarily, unless my father and I are entertaining, you'll be free every evening as soon as the dishes are done."

She nodded, taking it all in, eager to learn.

I went on. "Every morning at seven o'clock I'd like you to bring a tray with two cups of coffee on it to my room. I'll take my father's to him myself."

She didn't answer, but I had the feeling she'd do exactly what I said.

I went on then and told her that I would make out the menus and have them written down for her every day, and that I would write out her work schedule once a week. When I finished, she smiled at me and said, "This is such a help. I felt so worried when I came. I feel better now."

On her way out of my room she stopped at my bookcase and touched one of the books that was lying on top.

"I used to read a lot," she said. "My mother had books. They're gone now."

"What happened to them?" I asked her.

"When she died, my father sold them. I was ten then."

I couldn't decide whether she was regretting her mother's

death or the loss of the books. But I did know that I wanted to keep her in the house. She was a find. If she became dissatisfied and left, Aunt Helen would be finding someone else right away, and I wouldn't have such luck twice.

I said, "Would you like to take a book to your room to read?"

She said, "That would be nice, Dorrie. I'll be careful with it."

She spent a long time then handling my books, opening them, reading a little, and finally she chose *Wuthering Heights*, and I asked her if she'd ever read it before.

She said, "No, but the beginning looks good."

I envied her that she had her first reading of it still ahead. She said good night and went out, and I went back downstairs to be with my father.

He was dropping ice cubes in his glass, fixing himself a drink. Dinner seemed to have become only a temporary interruption to his evening's drinking. I didn't know what to do about it except to make him happier so he wouldn't want to drink so much.

"I think she's going to work out fine," I said.

He sipped his drink and then poured in a little more scotch and bobbed the ice cubes up and down with his finger.

"That's good, baby," he answered, but I wasn't at all sure he knew what I'd said to him.

"School will be starting soon, Daddy," I said. "Would you like to go away a little while before then—maybe for a weekend?"

He looked as though he were seeing me from a great distance and he said, "Go away? No, I don't think I want to go away. I don't know where we'd go."

I was afraid to mention the lake or anything to do with boating, I said, "We might drive up to Crampton. They'll be having the fall festival before long."

This time he didn't answer me. He got up as though he'd forgotten I was in the room, and carrying his glass, he went through the kitchen and out the back door. I went to his den and turned the light out and looked into the back yard. I could see him near the spiraea bushes sitting in the wicker chair in the dark. I couldn't bear to see him sitting there alone. I went to the phone and dialed the Stevensons' number.

"Virginia," I said, "this is Dorrie. Daddy and I were wondering if you and Dan felt like coming over for a while."

She said, "Why, sure, Dorrie. We're just sitting here doing nothing. Is everything all right?"

I was afraid I'd let the worry sound in my voice.

"Everything's fine," I said. "We just haven't seen you for a while."

I went to the kitchen and made coffee. While I was waiting for the water to boil, I thought of the parties we'd had at our house. Long ago I'd started hating them. Two or three times a year my parents would invite a lot of people in. My mother would stock up on all kinds of liquor and beer. She'd spend the day making hors d'oeuvres. The people who didn't want to drink too much would go home early. Sooner or later the kissing started.

I was in fourth grade the first time I saw it. My mother had gotten rid of me early. In spite of the loud talking and laughing and the record player going, she expected me to be able to sleep. She made a big thing of letting me stay downstairs until ten. Then she poured some Seven-Up into a glass and dropped a cherry in on the ice cubes and said, "Here's your nightcap, honey. You go on up to bed now like a good girl."

I undressed for bed, and even though I felt as though I were a million miles away from all of them. I felt as though the man I'd seen downstairs, dancing with one of the girls from his office, wasn't my father. My mother's party had changed him, made him into someone else.

I slid into bed, wishing that my father would come up to sit with me for a while. Finally I couldn't stand the lonesome feeling any longer and I put on my robe and went down the hall to the room at the head of the stairs. From the window there I could look down into the back yard where some of the people were acting silly, pretending to play croquet. The moonlight was bright enough so that I could see Dan Stevenson jumping around, acting like a child. But even if I couldn't have made him out, I would have recognized his big, booming voice yelling, "I got you. I got you. You're dead."

I settled down on the floor, watching what was going on below. I don't know how long it was before I heard someone coming up the stairs. I thought it might be my mother, so I half lay down under the window sill so she couldn't see me.

It was two people. I heard my father's voice. "Come here, baby," he said, and for an instant I thought he meant me. The girl from his office started kissing him then, and I wanted to run out into the hall and push her away from him and down the stairs. I saw her lying at the bottom with her neck broken and her eyes open, staring up into nothing—eyes that would never look at my father again.

My father said to her, "Wait here, baby. I've got to say good night to the kid."

He went into my room and after a moment he turned the light on in there, and then he went across the hall to my parents' room. When he came out he said to that woman, "I don't know where the little dickens has gotten to."

He stood for a moment in the doorway of the room I was in and then he saw me under the window and he said to her, "You go on downstairs. I'll be down later."

He came over to me and stooped down and said, "What's my baby doing in here?"

I started crying and I said, "I don't like her, Daddy."

"You mean Norene?" he asked. "You mustn't mind, baby. It's all in fun."

He pulled me up and took me into my room and kissed me good night and he said, "Some day you'll understand, Dorrie. It doesn't mean anything at all."

I knew he thought he was right and that it didn't mean anything to him. But I knew that kissing my father meant something to that woman. I don't know whether or not my father told my mother about it, but several times in the years after that I heard my mother say, "Dorrie's such a little prude. I don't know where she gets it."

The water was boiling now and I poured it into the dripolator and set cups and saucers on a tray. I divided the leftover pie into four pieces and put them on the pansy plates. Then I went out to my father.

"Daddy," I said, "the Stevensons are coming over to have coffee with us."

"Isn't it a little late?" he asked. "I was just leaving."

I sat down on the grass at his feet and put my head against his knee. "I wish you'd promise me something," I said. "I wish you'd stop going out there every night. It isn't good for you."

I felt his hand on my hair and he said, "All right, Dorrie. Maybe you're right. I won't go tonight."

I felt warm and close to him and I wished I hadn't invited the Stevensons and that my father and I could go on sitting there in the dark together.

But before long they drove into the driveway and the lights of their car flashed into the back yard. My father and I went to meet them.

In the living room I said, "I'll get the coffee."

Dan looked at me and in his big voice said, "Coffee? What's this coffee business?" He looked at my father then and said, "What's the matter, boy—have you gone on the wagon?"

Before my father could answer, I said, "The coffee's all ready. And I've got pie, apple pie."

Virginia said, "Why, I think that's fine, Dorrie. It sounds good to me. Let me help you."

I was grateful to Virginia for backing me up. We went into the kitchen and I thought I'd won. But while I was pouring the coffee, Dan and my father came out and Dan said, "You girls can have all the coffee you want. I'm having something stronger."

My father made martinis for Dan and just before he left the kitchen, he took a new bottle of scotch from the cupboard.

When we were settled in the living room, I looked at Virginia and said, "Have you read any good books lately?"

She sighed and said, "No, I dearly love to read. But I just don't have time."

I said, "I've been reading *Immortal Wife.* It's awfully good, one of the best books I've read in a long while."

I waited for one of them to ask me what it was about, but no one said anything.

I said, "It's a historical novel, based on the life of Jessie Frémont."

My father said, "Dan, I've been wondering if you'd do something for me."

"You name it, boy," Dan said.

"Well," my father said, "I want to sell that God-damned boat, but I never want to lay eyes on it again. Could you get rid of it for me?"

"Sure, I'll do it," Dan said. "Is it still at the lake?"

"Yes," my father answered. "It's docked at the Fairway Marina."

"What's it worth?" Dan asked.

"I don't know," my father said. "I've put a lot of equipment on it. Just get whatever you can."

Dan said, "I'll put an ad in the paper. I don't suppose this is the best time of year to sell a boat, though."

"I bought it myself in August," my father said. "People are looking for bargains now. I wish to hell I'd never seen the God-damned thing."

My father sat looking at the floor. Virginia said, "Yes, but there was no way of knowing." She stood up then and went to the kitchen and got herself a glass and came back and poured a martini.

"On top of pie and coffee?" Dan asked her.

She sounded angry. "Yes," she said, "on top of pie and coffee."

My father said, "Dorrie, where's that box of pictures?"

When I brought it in, they sat on the sofa together, looking through all the snapshots and photographs of my mother.

I knew right then that gradually I would put an end to our friendship with the Stevensons. We were never going to be a foursome. The three of them would forever be shutting me out —drinking and talking about my mother. I would find new friends for us.

I carried the dishes to the kitchen and put them in the dishwasher. When I told Dan and Virginia good night, it wasn't hard to smile at them. I knew that before long we wouldn't be seeing them any more.

Later I heard the three of them pile into the Stevensons' car and drive away. I knew where they had gone. My father had forgotten his promise. They'd made him forget it.

I lay in bed, not able to sleep, wanting something so much that I ached with the wanting. I wished that my father were back and that I could get up and go into his room and slip into bed with him.

Chapter 17

❧ ❧ ❧ ❧ ❧ ❧ ❧ ❧ ❧ ❧ ❧

Promptly at seven the next morning Anna was knocking on my door, bringing coffee for my father and me. I found I never had to tell her anything twice. And she kept her place, not trying to be a real part of the family. She was content to be on the outside. She spent her free time in her room, reading my books. She wasn't a particularly fast reader, but she was interested in almost any kind of fiction.

School had started and it had begun to get cooler, and my aunt came to the house to look through my winter clothes. She was in my room, holding my brown pleated skirt up to the light, when she said, "How's your father doing these days, Dorrie?"

I said, "A little better, I think. But he still goes to the cemetery every night."

She let out a sigh and said, "Poor Jim, your mother always was the strong one."

I didn't answer her, but when she asked me what night I wanted to go shopping, I told her Friday. But Monday night I went to town by myself. I called her when I got home and told her I'd already bought the things I needed.

She said, "Well, really, Dorrie. I went out of my way to get Mrs. Salley to take my part in Drama Club Friday night."

I didn't answer.

I had been careful with my father's money and had bought only shoes, a skirt, and two sweaters. As I hung my new skirt in the closet, I saw the gray shirtwaist. One Saturday morning about six months before, I was on one of those boring errands for my mother when I went past Bireley's Department Store and saw the dress on a mannequin in the window, and I knew I had to have it. It was a soft, pearl gray with little black buttons going down the front to the waist.

When I got home, I told my mother about it. She was in the kitchen making cheese straws and she brushed the hair up from her forehead with the back of her hand and said, "I don't know, Dorrie. I can't quite see gray on you."

I walked over and picked up one of the cheese straws and ate it.

"This is a very beautiful shade of gray," I said.

"We'll see." She turned around to put another cookie sheet in the oven.

But I was onto her game—put it off and she'll forget it.

"Let's go downtown this afternoon and look at it," I said.

"Really, Dorrie, you know the Stevensons are coming for dinner tonight."

"Then let me get it and bring it home on approval."

She frowned, and I stood there thinking that even when she was old she was going to be good-looking.

"Let's wait and ask Daddy," she said, "if he approves of gray for a girl your age, then you can bring it home Monday night after school and we'll see how it looks on you. It might not even fit, you know."

Through the rest of the morning and half of the afternoon about every half hour I'd say, "What about the dress?" or "I wish you'd just look at it today," or "It's the prettiest dress I ever saw."

Finally at two-thirty I went into her room. She had pulled down the blinds and was taking the nap she took every afternoon that she was home. I could see she was just dozing off and I said, "May I go get the dress now?"

She shot up in bed. "For heaven's sake," she said, "go get the dress. With your complexion you shouldn't wear gray, but if you're going to drive me crazy over it, go get it."

That was like her to take a crack at my complexion. Actually my skin was smooth and soft. But she was always saying, "Run out in the sunshine, Dorrie, I'd like to see some roses in those cheeks."

I wore the dress that night when the Stevensons came. My mother didn't want to let on she'd been mad, and she smiled and said, "It *is* a pretty shade of gray, Dorrie."

In September, when school started and there was a change in the season, it seemed to me there was a change in the atmosphere at our house too. My aunt had gotten rid of my mother's clothes. Anna had become an efficient part of the background, doing her work quickly and well, but never intruding herself on my father and me. And there was a slight change in my father's mood. Sometimes he started a conversation and we would talk for five or ten minutes. He still went to the cemetery, but not so often. One evening I told him one of the silly ding-dong jokes that were going around school, and he slapped his knee and laughed with me in a way I hadn't seen since the accident.

More and more I had the feeling that there was something wonderful ahead for us. Something more than my fixing his drink and getting out his cigar and laughing together over a joke. Something that even I couldn't yet define. Being in the bubble together was going to be part of it, but not all. Being in the bubble was going to mean more than even I knew.

Sandy came after me every morning and we walked to school together. I didn't get involved with the other kids any more than I ever had. My Spanish teacher asked me to stay after class one night.

"Dorrie," she said, "you're my prize pupil. I do wish you'd

join Spanish Club. You'd enjoy it, really you would, and we need you."

"I couldn't possibly," I said. "My mother died, you know. I have a lot of responsibility at home."

"Come, now, Dorrie," she said. "I'm sure you could spare an hour once a month."

"Maybe I could, Miss Corrington, but I never join any clubs. I think they're silly."

She got up from her desk and started stacking papers. "All right, Dorrie, no one's going to make you do it. But I've watched you shut yourself away from the other students for years. I'm afraid it's a great mistake."

Several times during September, Virginia Stevenson called. I sometimes let Anna answer the telephone, but first I gave her instructions.

"Anna," I said, "my father's been through a great deal. He needs peace and quiet, and people don't realize that. Whenever anyone phones and asks for him, call me first. That way I can give him only the calls he would want to have."

"All right, Dorrie," she said, and she was very good about it. She didn't lie to people. When they asked for my father, she simply said, "Just a moment, please," and then she called me. I had the feeling that she approved of the way I protected my father and that actually she was fond of me. But she never tried to come close. I got in the habit of putting aside for her books that I thought she would particularly enjoy. She never took advantage. I was amused and flattered one day when I came home from school and saw that she had cut bangs like mine. It was the first sign that she took any interest in her appearance aside from being clean and neat. The bangs happened to be becoming to her, but I had the feeling she'd have worn them regardless, just because I did.

Every time Virginia Stevenson called I gave her some excuse for our not coming to see them or having them over.

Finally late in September she said, "Well, listen now, Dorrie, it seems to me you and Jim are awfully busy all of a sudden."

I said, "To tell you the truth, Virginia, my father didn't particularly care for the way Dan handled the boat sale."

"What on earth do you mean?" she asked.

"The boat was worth a good deal more than Dan got for it."

"Why, Dorrie Lawson," she said, "we spent Sunday after Sunday at the lake getting the best deal we could for your father."

I knew how maddening silence could be and I didn't answer. After about a minute, in a hurt voice, she said, "Good-by, Dorrie," and hung up.

I began to get an uneasy feeling that she and Dan would come over uninvited that evening. As soon as we had finished eating dinner, I said to my father, "Daddy, let's go and see Grandma tonight. I want to take her some marigolds before the frost gets them."

We stayed at Grandma's until quite late, and sure enough, when we came home Anna told me the Stevensons had been there.

I went into my father's bedroom and said, "Daddy, have you noticed Dan and Virginia haven't been to see us much since they sold the boat?"

He was putting his cuff links in the shell dish next to the wedding picture. "Why, yes, I guess that's right," he said. "We can invite them over soon if you want to."

"I don't think they particularly want to be invited. I think they feel guilty."

"I can't imagine why they'd feel guilty," he said.

"I can. They didn't begin to get the money they could have for the boat. It was your money and they didn't care."

"Oh, come now, Dorrie," he said. "The Stevensons are our *friends*. You mustn't talk about them like that."

"I don't care," I said. "The boat was worth a lot more than they got."

"That may be," he said, "but they were selling at the wrong time of year. I'm sure Dan did his best."

The next evening while we were eating the phone rang and Anna came back into the dining room and looked at me and said, "Telephone, Dorrie."

It was Dan, and he said, "Hello, Dorrie. It was your father I wanted to speak to."

"He's not here," I said. "Could I take a message for him?" Dan's voice boomed over the wire. "I don't know what's going on over there, but I'm not taking this lying down. We've been friends too long. You tell your father I'm coming over there and I'll wait all night to see him if I have to."

"I don't think I'd do that, Dan," I said. "I think you'd be wise to wait until the whole thing blows over."

"I'm not waiting. I've got nothing to hide and I'm not waiting."

"All right," I said and hung up.

I went back to the table and tried to eat, but my hands were shaking and I gave up. The bone-handled carving knife was on the meat platter right in front of me and I could feel it in my hand, slashing and slashing until the Stevensons lay there motionless and never bothered us again.

My father said, "What's wrong, Dorrie? You don't look well."

"I'm all right," I said, and I did feel better because it wasn't often that my father noticed how I looked.

About an hour later the Stevensons drove into the driveway. Anna had finished in the kitchen and was in her room, reading. My father was having his first scotch of the evening's drinking. To show I had nothing to be afraid of, I went to the door and said hello and let them in.

My father got up, smiling, and held out his hand to Dan and

said, "Well, it's about time you showed up. Where've you been keeping yourself?"

Dan said, "Jim, I don't want to beat about the bush. I want you to tell me right out what's on your mind."

His voice was quieter than usual and he stood there unsmilingly, looking at my father.

"For God's sake," my father said, "what are you talking about?"

"This business about the boat. About my not getting enough for it."

My father looked from Dan to me and then he said, "What is this? What's going on?"

"I'll tell you what's going on," Dan said. "This business of your avoiding us, of not coming to the phone when we call. And Dorrie telling Ginny we didn't get enough for the boat. I don't like it, Jim."

My father said, "There's some misunderstanding. Let's calm down now and get this straightened out. In the first place, I've never avoided you on the phone. I'd have no reason to."

"What about tonight?" Dan asked. "Weren't you home for dinner? I called right at six and Dorrie said you were gone. You don't call that avoiding us?"

My father said, "Let's all sit down." He pulled one of the Morris chairs over a little for Virginia, and Dan and I sat on the sofa.

Then my father looked at me. "Did you say I wasn't home tonight, Dorrie?" he asked.

"I didn't want your dinner interrupted," I said. "I think it's rude of people to call at mealtime."

Virginia said, "What about the other times, Dorrie? Time and again this month I've called, trying to get you and Jim to come over for dinner. I never get to speak to your father and I get nothing but excuses from you."

"We've been busy," I said.

She went on, "And then you tell me your father thought Dan didn't get enough for the boat."

"Dorrie," my father said, "I want you to tell Dan and Virginia right now in front of me that I never said any such thing."

I could hardly bear the way my father was looking at me. They had pushed us far apart, making a great distance between us. I've thought since that they had a lot to do with the way things finally ended.

"My father didn't say it," I said, and I got up and left them and went to my room. I felt as though my father would never like me again. I felt far away from the bubble. I didn't turn the light on in my room; I just lay on the bed in the darkness feeling terrible. Finally the words of a poem started coming to me from somewhere and I got up and wrote them down.

Don't decide that you can go away from me
And leave me standing tall and strong.
I won't be tall or strong
If you go away.
I will only be alone.

The Stevensons stayed for several hours and I knew that everything was all right between the three of them again. I undressed for bed and turned out the duck lamp. I sat in my rocker by the window then and I wanted my father there in the darkness with me, saying, "It's all right, baby."

When they left, I heard him come up the stairs, but instead of coming on down the hall, he knocked on the door of Anna's room. My door was part way open and I could hear what he said.

"Anna, I understand you've been referring all telephone calls to Dorrie, even when people are asking for me."

"Why, yes," she said, "I have. Dorrie didn't want you bothered."

"Well, from now on," my father told her, "if anyone asks for me, I want to know about it."

"All right, Mr. Lawson," she said, and he came on down the hall toward my room.

"Dorrie," he called.

"Yes, Daddy," I said and got up and turned on the light.

He came into the room, and I sat on my bed and he sat in my rocker. "Dorrie, I'm worried about you," he said. "I'm afraid I can't see it any other way but that you lied to the Stevensons. I've never known you not to tell the truth."

"I'm sorry, Daddy," I said.

"But why did you do it? What reason was there? The Stevensons have always been crazy about you."

"I don't know, Daddy," I said. I looked down at the floor. "I don't know why I did it."

He sighed and looked as if he didn't know what to say or do. He got up and walked over to the window and looked out at the street light below.

Then he came back by my bed and said, "It's time you were asleep, regardless. Tomorrow's a school day." He had started to turn out the duck lamp when he saw my poem. He picked it up and read it and then he turned to me and said, "Oh, God, baby, I know how you feel. But she didn't want to leave us. You've got to understand that."

I knew there was no point in trying to tell him that the poem was written for him, not my mother. I wanted to say, "All right, Daddy," but I couldn't get the words out. After a moment he turned out the light and patted my shoulder and said, "Go to sleep now," and left the room.

That night the dream was the old one. I was walking down the street with my father and everything was nice and then there was the big hole with the spits turning around down in it and I was going to fall and my father was gone.

Did I imagine it the next morning, or was there a change in Anna's attitude toward me? There was nothing I could put my finger on. She did everything she had before, except that she no longer gave me my father's telephone calls. All I know is that some time in the next few months, subtly and almost unnoticed by me at the time, I began to feel less the mistress of the house.

I dreaded the next time the Stevensons would come to see us knowing that by getting caught lying I had weakened myself.

One night after school my father said, "Dorrie, I think it would be a nice gesture if you called Virginia and invited them over. Just to show there are no hard feelings."

When they came, both of them hugged me. I hated them for being in a position to forgive me. Ever since my mother died, people had been hugging me and I was sick of it. I walked across the room to stir the fire I'd built earlier, and my movements were awkward and stiff.

"How are things going at school?" Virginia asked.

"Fine," I said.

Virginia took my chair opposite my father's, and rather than sit on the sofa with Dan, I sat on the hearth.

Dan smiled at me and said, "Little Dorrie Sit by the Fire."

I hated their patronizing, and then, what was even worse, my father said to me, "Dorrie, honey, I wonder if you'd like to share your poem with Dan and Virginia?"

"All right, Daddy," I said, and I went to my room and took it from the drawer in which I now kept my poetry.

Downstairs I handed it to my father. He read it again and then silently handed it to Virginia. If she had given her honest opinion, she would have said something like, "It doesn't rhyme." But instead she read and reread it and gazed at me and breathed, "It's beautiful. Perfectly beautiful." Dan put on a similar performance, only in his louder voice.

Then Virginia said, "But you know, Dorrie, you *are* tall and strong. And you're not alone, really you're not. Even though at times it may seem that way."

"That's right, baby," my father said. "I know I can't take your mother's place. I wouldn't even try. But you still have your old dad."

Have I, Daddy, have I? I wanted to ask him. Do I have you? It doesn't feel as though I do. It feels as if Dan and Virginia have you, and my mother has you. It doesn't feel as though I have you.

"Dorrie wrote this the last night you were here," my father said to Dan.

"You just forget all about that night," Dan said. "It's all gone and in the past, water over the mill."

"That's right, honey," Virginia said. "Don't think we don't know what you've been through. We know how you want your mother."

Suddenly I jumped up and ran up the stairs to my bathroom and closed the door and vomited. If I hadn't vomited, I wouldn't have been able to keep the words from screaming out of me. "I hated her. I hated her. I hated her."

My father came to the bathroom door and said, "Are you all right, Dorrie?"

By that time I could control my voice and I said, "Yes, Daddy, I'm all right. For a moment I felt a little sick."

"All right, baby," he said and went back to the Stevensons.

That was about a month before Christmas, and I've never been sure that this wasn't the beginning of the illness I had later. Can words that aren't said make you sick? Lots of times after that evening with the Stevensons I didn't feel well.

Chapter 18

When Christmas came, Anna went home for the holidays, and my aunt invited us for dinner. Ordinarily at our house we had a Christmas tree in the living room, but I put the beautiful blue spruce which my father and I had bought in the sun porch. I didn't use any of the old decorations. I bought all new red lights and red balls, and even though I hated the expense, I felt it was worth it. There was no need to remind my father of past Christmases.

I had three different presents for my father. I bought him a beautiful calfskin billfold, much more expensive than the one he'd been given the previous Christmas. And I knitted him a bright red scarf. But best of all, I went to town early in December and had a photograph of myself made for him.

Daddy liked the presents. I could tell that. He thanked me several times. He put the scarf around his neck and went to the mirror in the hall and said, "It's beautiful, Dorrie."

"I made it myself," I said.

He took the scarf off and folded it.

"And from now on," I said, "I'm going to start knitting your socks. They're giving lessons down at Bireley's."

"That's fine, baby," he said.

He got out his old billfold my mother had given him and he looked sad and I could tell he was remembering her. Then he took his cards and money and the picture of her out of it and put them in his new billfold. I wished I'd had a small picture made of myself too.

When he opened the photograph of me, he smiled and said, "You're getting to be a young lady, Dorrie. I can't realize it."

My father had bought me a beautiful pink sweater and skirt. I hugged him and went to my room to try them on. They fit exactly, and I thought he must have been noticing me more than usual to know my size. I went downstairs walking like a model. I went into the living room where my father was and stopped and then walked on a few steps and stopped again, twisting and turning the way models do. Only recently I'd had to buy a larger size brassière, and I knew the sweater looked good on me.

My father smiled again and said, "Yes, you are getting to be quite a young lady."

I hugged him and put my cheek against his and said, "Oh, Daddy, we're going to be so happy together. As soon as I get through high school, I won't do anything but take care of you."

He chuckled and said, "I've an idea some boy will come along and change your mind about that."

"Daddy," I said, "those silly boys. You're worth a hundred of them."

We ate breakfast that morning on trays in front of the fireplace, and when we finished my father said, "What time are we to go to Helen's?"

I said, "At two. I wish we didn't have to go. I wish we could have our dinner here alone."

He smiled and said, "Your aunt has to do her duty by us, you know. She wouldn't feel right if she didn't."

Around eleven o'clock he put his coat on and came into the kitchen.

"I'll be back before long," he said.

Suddenly the happiness I'd felt was gone and I said, "Where are you going, Daddy?"

"To the cemetery," he said. He sounded almost as though he felt ashamed.

"On Christmas?" I asked. "Do you really have to go on Christmas?"

"I haven't been for a long time, Dorrie," he said. "It's been two weeks. Today I keep thinking of her."

"But she's not there, Daddy," I said. "She's gone. She won't be back."

His eyes held the old pained look that I'd seen so often through that fall.

"I'm here, Daddy. I'm alive, up walking around and alive. I need you. Don't leave me alone on Christmas."

He didn't go, but I didn't really win. Several times during the day I could tell he was thinking of her. I wondered what Christmas he remembered best. I wondered if he remembered what happened the year he gave me my sled. He put my snowsuit and my mittens and my boots on me and we went outside and he pulled me across the snow. But I wasn't afraid. After a long time we were flying. We went so fast that I felt we stopped at the Stevensons. Virginia gave me hot chocolate and my father and Dan drank eggnog and we were all happy together. I fell asleep, and when I woke up my father was putting my snowsuit on me and then we went flying over the snow together back to our house. My mother was angry. She was angry at my father and me.

She said, "I waited and waited. I think the chicken's completely ruined."

My father said, "I'm sorry, Eleanore. Dan and I got to talking. You know how it is."

After only a little while she wasn't angry any longer. But I never forgot that when she was, my father and I had been in something together.

I wore my pink sweater and skirt to Aunt Helen's that day. I had on the My Sin perfume and I had changed my hair back to the French roll.

When my father and I walked in, everyone started saying the usual Merry Christmases. Harry was home from military school. Military school was one more attempt on my aunt's part to make a man out of Harry.

My aunt took our coats and looked me over in my new clothes and said, "What a perfect fit, Dorrie. They said I could bring them back if they weren't right." She wasn't content to let me think my father had chosen my new sweater and skirt for me.

When my father and I walked into the living room, Harry and another uniformed boy jumped to attention and I half expected them to salute. Harry had changed not only his style of moving but his style of speaking too.

He said, "Dorrie, Uncle Jim, may I present Elliot Whelan?"

Elliot's bow was so military I could almost hear the clanking of swords. I could hardly hide my amusement.

My father shook hands with them. When we were seated, my father said, "Well, Harry, how do you like the military life?"

"Fine, sir," Harry said. "It's great, sir."

My father looked at Harry's friend and said, "Where is your home, Elliot?"

"St. Louis, sir," Elliot said.

For half an hour this went on. They sirred my father almost to death. Finally my aunt came to the door and said, "Dorrie, do you want to help me put things on the table?"

As I started to leave the room, I caught my father's eye and gave him an amused look, but he didn't catch what I meant and he only smiled at me.

When we had eaten, my aunt said, "Harry, why don't you and Dorrie show Elliot the town? You can take the car."

I said, "You two go on. I'll have to be getting home with my father."

Daddy said, "Oh, you go with them, Dorrie. I'll be all right. They can bring you home later."

I said, "I'd really rather not."

But he didn't seem to know how I felt. He said, "Now I can't have you spending all your Christmas vacation with an old fogey like me." He looked at Harry and Elliot then and said, "But you two young whippersnappers take good care of her."

"We will, sir," they said, almost together.

The ride was as boring as I had expected. Pale winter sunlight lay over the dead Christmas afternoon. Harry drove by the Baptist Seminary and the empty swimming pool and down the lifeless main street. The only thing even slightly amusing about the ride was that Elliot's efforts to impress me were as laughable as his military manner with my father had been.

He said to Harry, "You call this a city? Man, you ought to see St. Louis. We've got some real jumping places."

Harry said, "Oh, I don't know. You ought to see the Dine-a-mite on Saturday nights. There's plenty of action."

"I'll bet," Elliot said. "I'll just bet."

"We'll show you," Harry said. "Won't we, Dorrie? Would your dad let you go out there sometime or is it too wild?"

"Hardly too wild!" I yawned. "But a little juvenile. My father knows I've outgrown all that."

"I knew it!" Elliot said. "I took one look at you and I said to myself, 'Here's a doll who's been around.'"

"I know what." Harry's voice was tense with excitement. "Let's go out there New Year's Eve. How about it, Dorrie?"

"My father and I have New Year's Eve plans," I said.

"He'd let you off," Harry said. "He's a good egg."

"Harry," I said, "don't you understand? I don't want to go to the Dine-a-mite with you and Elliot."

"You've got another date," Elliot said.

Then it dawned on me that this ridiculous puppet in a uniform actually expected me to be his date.

I laughed. "I have no date," I said. "I want no date. I'll see the new year in with my father. I can get you a date, though, Elliot, if you like."

"Who?" Harry sounded suspicious.

"Sandy Donovan," I said.

"For Pete's sake," Harry said. "That creep!"

I had known almost exactly what he would say. I said, "All right, Hairy Ape, if that's the way you talk about my best friend, you take me home right now."

Elliot sniggered and said, "Hairy Ape," and I said, "I mean it, Harry. I want to go home."

When we came to my house, Harry said, "Don't be sore, Dorrie," and Elliot leered at me and said, "I'm not giving up. You and I could have fun, doll."

My father was in the living room, drinking and looking into the almost dead fire.

I stirred the fire and put another log on it and went to the kitchen to fix sandwiches. I got him to eat part of one, but then he went back to his drink.

Pretty soon he said, "I stopped by your grandma's on the way home. She's not at all well, Dorrie."

I said, "Is it the headaches again?"

He said, "No, worse. It's heartbreaking. I could hardly stand it. She doesn't remember that your mother's gone."

That's just what he needs, I thought bitterly. That's just exactly what he needs, someone who thinks my mother's still alive.

When we were ready to go upstairs, I picked up the picture I'd given him and said, "Do you want me to take this up to your room?"

He said, "Why, yes, I guess so."

I put it on the bureau by the wedding picture. He was taking off his tie and he said, "I'll be going after Annie tomorrow."

"Annie?" I asked.

"Anna," he said.

I kissed him good night and went to my room, wondering what had made him call her Annie. But then I thought of Little Orphan Annie and Little Annie Roonie and I knew that Annie was a natural for our Anna. She was the orphan, on the outside.

Chapter 19

᪐᪐᪐᪐᪐᪐᪐᪐᪐᪐

When my father came home from the office the next afternoon, he smiled at me and in a teasing way said, "It seems you've made a conquest, Dorrie."

"Who's that?" I asked.

"This boy, this friend of Harry's, thinks you're quite a girl. Helen called me at the office. She's getting up a little party for the kids on New Year's Eve, and this boy wants you for his date."

I was furious at my aunt.

I said, "Daddy, I can't stand that boy. He's nothing but a braggart and a show-off."

"Now, Dorrie," he said, "I thought he was a nice kid."

"Daddy, you don't know," I said. "He's pushy. I've already told him I wouldn't have a date with him. I told him I was going to spend New Year's Eve with you."

My father looked worried. "Helen says you spend too much time with me," he said. "She thinks you need to be with people your own age."

"That sounds like Helen," I said. "She always knows what's right for everyone else."

"She has your best interest at heart," my father said. "I don't know but what she's right about it."

"Daddy," I said, "don't you want to spend New Year's Eve with me?"

He said, "Now you know that's not the question at all, baby. It's you I'm thinking of."

"Well, then, just forget everything Helen says. We don't need her telling us what to do."

My father still looked worried, and I went up to him and put one hand on either side of his face and said, "Don't worry, Daddy, darling. We don't need Helen or anyone else."

He patted my shoulder and said, "We'll see," and he smiled at me, but I could tell my aunt's words were bothering him. When we had eaten, we drove out to get Anna. She sat in the back seat, and the words Little Orphan Annie kept going through my mind.

"Did you have a good Christmas, Anna?" my father asked.

"Yes, fine," she said. "But it's good to be coming back." She gave a little laugh and added, "I guess I'm getting used to town."

My father smiled at her over his shoulder. "It's good to have you back," he said.

"Thank you," she said, and I could tell by her voice that she didn't know he was only being polite.

"Yes, Anna," I said, "I've been so busy with Christmas, I've hardly touched the house."

That night Virginia Stevenson phoned my father. I heard him say, "Yes, that'd be fine, Virginia. I'd like that. I don't know about Dorrie. She may have other plans."

"What was that all about, Daddy?" I asked.

"Oh, Virginia thought I might like to come over New Year's Eve. They're having a bunch in."

"She didn't invite me?" I asked.

"Dorrie," he said, "I want you to do something for me. I want you to go to Helen's party. You can't tell, you might have a wonderful time with the other kids."

It wasn't often that my father said, "I want you to do something for me," and when he did, I couldn't refuse him. But I had never hated my aunt more. I decided right then that she would never regret making me have a date with that stupid boy. My father would see he couldn't trust her judgment.

I said, "All right, Daddy, I'll do it."

He laughed and said, "Now, baby, don't act like it's the end of the world. There could be worse things than going to a party and having a good time with kids your own age."

The afternoon of New Year's Eve I said to Anna, "I thought you'd want to be home tonight."

She said, "No, we never made anything of New Year's Eve on the farm."

I said, "Well, my father and I are going to different parties. But we want to have a little supper alone together to celebrate ahead of time. You understand, don't you?"

She said, "Of course, Dorrie. Is there anything special you'd like to have me fix for you to eat?"

I said, "No. In fact, I thought you might like to take the afternoon and evening off. There's a good movie at the Downtown."

She said, "That's nice of you, but I think I'll stay home and read. I've finished all of your books. Would it be all right for me to take one from the living room?"

I said, "Yes, but I don't believe I'd bother the ones in the den. They're my father's."

I had never cooked in the chafing dish, but I took out my recipe book and saw that it was easy. I set everything up on the coffee table in the living room and when my father came home, I was ready to put together the butter and cheese and ale.

He smiled at me and said, "Well, it looks like we're having a pre-party party here."

"Yes," I said, "our own little private party."

When the Welsh rabbit was almost cooked, I set our places at the gate-legged table. My father was on his second scotch, and I wished I were going to be with him that night to watch his drinking.

When I said, "It's ready, Daddy," he looked at the table and said, "What about Anna?"

I said, "She's already eaten. I gave her the evening off. She's in her room, reading."

He said, "I wonder sometimes if she doesn't get lonely. She doesn't seem to have made friends."

I said, "Oh, she and Mrs. Berkson gossip back and forth. They have a lot in common."

"I wouldn't have thought so," he said. "Anyway, Dorrie, you've been awfully good to her, teaching her how we do things, giving her books to read. I've noticed the effort you've made. I know you didn't really want a housekeeper."

For the first time in quite a while I thought of Mrs. Mason. I wished I could remember some other expression on her face than the horrified one I'd seen when I'd limped down the hall at her. But I couldn't remember her any other way. I shook off the superstitious feeling that came to me that some day I might really have to limp. I reminded myself that it was she who was crippled, not I.

Elliot Whelan had phoned that he and Harry would be after me at nine. When it was time for me to get dressed, I thought of dragging out an old plaid jumper that I hadn't worn in years. I thought of wearing it and making myself look as ugly as I could. But I couldn't quite do it. There would be other people at the party and they would know that I was Jim Lawson's daughter and I had to look my best. And anyway, I was going to make something happen that night—what, I had no idea— but something that would cause my aunt to regret engineering my going to the party. If I looked my best, I would have more control over what happened.

I put on my cocktail-length party dress, fastened the plastic cape around my neck, and brushed my hair into the French roll. Ordinarily I didn't wear mascara, but now I carefully darkened my lashes. I remembered my mother saying, when I wanted to wear mascara, "But, honey, that would be like gilding the lily." It was true that my lashes were already dark, but I wanted to live up to Elliot Whelan's picture of me. He thought I was sophisticated and wild. I had the feeling that somehow I would use this idea of his to advantage.

Except for her wedding ring, my mother had only costume jewelry. I put on her rhinestone necklace and bracelet and they glittered like diamonds against the ice blue of my dress. I was glad I was ready early, and I went downstairs to my father.

"How do I look, Daddy?" I asked.

"You look beautiful, honey," he said. The look he gave me was fond and tender, but I saw his eyes on the rhinestones and, too late, I knew I had let my mother into the evening. I wondered if he and the Stevensons would spend the night talking about her.

I said, "Promise me something, Daddy. Promise that tonight at midnight you'll drink a toast to me. And I'll do the same to you, exactly at midnight."

"I'll do better than that," he said. "I'll drink a toast to you right now, and what's more, this sophisticated young lady I see before me is old enough to have a little glass of sherry. How about that?"

It had come sooner than I expected. I had thought it might be years before I would have a drink with my father. He went into the kitchen and came back carrying a tray with two glasses of sherry on it. We stood in front of the fireplace and held our glasses up to each other. "To my handsome father," I said, and he said, "To my beautiful daughter." We looked at each other while we sipped the yellow liquid. Happiness was all over me.

I wouldn't have been surprised to know that light was springing out from inside of me. I felt as though I could go into a dark room and light it up.

I thought, this is the beginning of a tradition in our house. Through all of the years together, the rest of our lives, every New Year's Eve, our first drink will be sherry.

My father finished his before I did. I wanted mine to last. He said, "I'm afraid scotch is really my drink."

"It's going to be mine, too," I said.

He smiled and said, "Not for a while, baby. A glass of sherry on New Year's Eve is just about right for you."

"I know," I said, "but, oh, Daddy, I'm growing up fast. Before you know it, I'm going to be grown up. Then we'll drink scotch together. We'll do all kinds of things together."

I didn't really like the smile he gave me. There was something sad about it.

He said, "When you grow up, you'll be leaving your old dad. You'll be going away to college or getting married, and that's the way it should be."

"Never," I said. "I'm never going to leave you."

"You'll see, baby," he said. "You'll see. You're young now. Your ideas will change."

I didn't try to convince him. It was enough that I knew.

I felt so happy about our toast that when the boys came after me, I didn't mind too much having to go to the party. Neither Elliot nor Harry wore their uniforms, and in leaving them off, they seemed also to have left off their stiff, formal manners.

I kissed my father good-by and said, "Have a good time and don't be late."

He said to Elliot, "Take care of my little girl now."

"I will, sir," Elliot said, and he held out his arm and we went to the car.

As we drove to Harry's house, "Take care of my little girl"

changed in my mind to "Take care of my big girl" to "Take care of my girl." I would be my daddy's girl. He would never need any other. And after this night he would never send me to a party with someone else. He would learn, as would my aunt, that I knew best.

My aunt had spent hours decorating their recreation room in the basement. Red and white and green streamers floated down from the ceiling. There were huge balloons and paper hats and horns and snappers. The furniture was pushed back to the walls, and several kids I knew from school were dancing. The music was the loud, banging kind that sounds as if it's trying to drum happiness into you. Against one wall, on a long table, there were cokes and ginger ale and ice and potato chips and several kinds of dip.

My aunt hugged me and said, "Happy New Year, darling," and went upstairs soon after that. She had set the stage and picked the actors. I was surprised that she was content to let us play our roles the way we chose.

Elliot came back from hanging up my coat and said, "Wanta dance, doll?"

We danced and I felt sorry for the kids who had to have music to make them happy. I was glad I wasn't like them, wanting to go to all the parties, trying to be popular and being worried about dates. I closed my eyes and remembered my dream of dancing with my father across the sand at the beach. I kept my eyes closed and my father's arms were around me.

The music ended, and I must have looked dazed when I opened my eyes and saw Elliot beside me. He put his arm around my waist and gave me a squeeze and said, "You were gone, doll, real gone."

We walked to the table and he handed me a coke. I said, "Is that the best you can do on New Year's Eve?"

He said, "Gosh, Dorrie, it's all we've got."

I sighed and said, "I knew I shouldn't have come."

He said, "You just come up to St. Louis sometime. I'll give you something besides coke."

I said, "Well, anyway, I'm glad I had a drink with my father before I left home."

"Here," I said, handing the coke back to him, "this isn't what I thought you had in mind when you asked me for a date. I thought you were a big-city boy."

"Dorrie," he said, "I'm a stranger in town. I didn't know where to get anything."

"It really wouldn't be too hard," I said. "Of course, if you dared to."

"Dared to," he said. "You just tell me where."

"It's so easy, it's laughable," I said.

"Okay, where? Where do I go?" His eyes were shining. He was ready.

"Just upstairs, that's all. In my aunt's liquor cupboard. If you dared to sneak it past her, of course."

"What would Harry say?" he asked.

"Harry!" I said. "Who's going to tell Hairy Ape? Coke's his speed. I thought you said you were two years older than he. Of course, if you're afraid . . ."

"Who's afraid?" he asked. He put his arm around my waist and gave me another squeeze. "You'll see, doll, we're two of a kind."

He started up the stairs and then turned back and said, "Where's the liquor?"

"In the cupboard over the refrigerator," I whispered.

I sat down on the bottom step to wait for him, and Ralph Reardon, one of the boys from school, came over and asked me to dance.

"Thanks," I said, "but I'm waiting for Elliot."

"Come on, Dorrie," he said. "The place isn't so big he won't find you."

Across the room I saw Janice Willowby watching Ralph. What she saw in him I couldn't imagine, but for two years they'd been going steady, and now she looked as though she were about to give a tug on his leash.

I looked up at Ralph and smiled and made my eyes have that "I like you" look and said, "You're right, Ralphie, he'll find me."

Each glimpse I had of Janice's face while Ralph and I danced told me she was getting madder all the time. Elliot came back downstairs and I could tell by the awkward way he held his right arm that he had a bottle under his coat.

I said, "Ralph, Elliot's back."

He said, "What's that guy got, Dorrie? You never gave any of us a second look. What's wrong with the home-town boys?"

I laughed and said, "There's nothing wrong with you, Ralphie. Now dance me over to Elliot."

I stood beside Elliot and watched Ralph go back to Janice. I could tell the little fool was bawling him out. I knew that if I put my mind to it, I could create a very interesting situation before the party was over and stir up a scene that would leave an impression on my aunt's mind. But Elliot was the date my aunt had pushed me into. Whatever happened had to happen with him.

Elliot said, "I got it. She didn't even know I was upstairs."

"Why'd you bring it down here?" I asked. "We can't drink it here."

His eyes widened, and he said, "Where, then? Baby, it's cold outside."

I said, "It's not cold in my aunt's car. Not with the heater running."

"I don't know, doll," he said. "Harry's got the key."

"Tell him you just want to go up to the corner for some Seven-Up. Tell him you're tired of coke. Then ask me to go along."

At first Harry hesitated. "Gee, Elliot," he said, "Mom's aw-fully particular about her car."

"Look, Harry," Elliot said, "just to the corner. For Pete's sake, I thought we were friends."

"Okay, okay," Harry took the car key from his pocket. "But be careful."

"You come, too, Dorrie," Elliot said. "I'll get your coat."

While Elliot was gone, Janice Willowby walked by me on the way to the bathroom. As she went past, she said in a low voice, "Stabbed anyone lately, Dorrie?"

I gave her my sweetest smile. Then I went up the stairs and left Elliot to bring the bottle and the coats. The only sign of my aunt was the light on in her bedroom and the sound of the tele-vision set. I motioned to Elliot that the coast was clear, and we got safely outside.

Elliot started the motor of the car and unscrewed the bottle top and handed it to me. It was bourbon and I hated the spoiled, sour taste. I swallowed almost none and handed it back to him.

"You're not much of a drinker," he said.

I said, "I started before you did. You'll have to catch up."

He tipped the bottle back and drank so much that I knew he wasn't used to drinking.

He pulled me over to him and I said, "Not now. Wait until we get parked somewhere."

In the darkness I couldn't see his face, and I never did know whether or not he'd planned to leave my aunt's driveway.

I said, "You're so much more sophisticated than Harry. The fellows in this town don't know how to have any fun."

He started backing the car and he said, "But we do, doll. We do."

A block from the house he said, "You wanta stop by the Dine-a-mite a while?"

I said, "That kid place?"

He said, "You're right, doll. We don't need them. We don't need nobody."

He drove past the Dine-a-mite and onto the highway south of town. He turned down the first little road he came to, pulled over to one side, and stopped the car.

He got out of the car and took off his coat and threw it on the back seat. He said, "Here, honey, let's take yours off."

"Not yet," I said. "I'm still cold."

He handed me the bottle. "Here," he said, "this will warm you up."

This time I swallowed none at all, but he didn't notice. Again he drank too much at once.

I said, "See if you can get some music," and he fooled around with the dial and finally got some vocalist moaning about his broken heart.

Then he put his arm around me and pulled me over to him, and while he was kissing me his other hand was on my knee and up my leg and I thought of my father. I pushed him away and said, "Wait. I need a drink."

"A drink for my doll," he said, and already his words weren't coming out right.

He drank again and recapped the bottle and set it on the floor.

"Come on now, honey," he said. "Let's take off your coat."

I let him take off my coat. I knew he wasn't particularly bright, but I could hardly believe he didn't know how ridiculous he looked to me. He threw my coat on the back seat and then he started feeling my breast and murmuring, "Um, that's cute. That's just cute," and then he felt of the other and said, "You mean they're two? Oh, baby, you're nice."

Pretty soon he took my hand and pushed it down on the hardness between his legs and said, "Here, honey, that's what I've got for you. It's yours, honey. It's all yours."

I couldn't see my watch and I didn't know just what time it was, but I knew that if I were going to be with my father at midnight, I'd better be getting home.

I said, "Elliot, I drank too much. I'm going to vomit."

He said, "Jesus, what a time to get sick."

He wasn't moving very fast, but he did manage to reach over and open the door on my side. I got out and he did, too, and I took his arm and walked a little way down the road, my head down, not talking. Then I turned back toward the car and said, "I think if I could just lie down a few minutes, I'd be all right."

He opened the car door and I crawled in on the seat. I said, "Here, you better put your coat on."

When I reached to the back seat for his coat, I pushed down the lock button on the back door. I handed him his coat and said, "Let me close this door. I'm freezing."

When he stepped back, I pulled the door shut and locked it. Then I locked both doors on the other side and started the car. I heard him yell and he started to run after the car, still yelling. I drove down the road until I found a place to turn around. As I drove back toward the highway, I could see Elliot standing in the middle of the road, daring me to run over him. He jumped out of the way at the last possible moment.

I drove to the Dine-a-mite, went in, and dialed the Stevensons' residence. There was so much noise, I could hardly hear Dan's voice. When he had called my father to the phone for me, I said, "Daddy, I'm at the Dine-a-mite. Could you come after me?"

My father said, "Did you say the Dine-a-mite?"

"Yes, Daddy," I said. "Something terrible happened."

He said, "Are you all right?"

"Yes," I said, "but please come."

"You stay right there," my father said. "I'm leaving now."

I stood in the front entrance and watched for my father. In only a few minutes he drove in, and the car had hardly stopped before he was out of it and running toward me.

"Are you all right, baby?" he cried.

"Yes, Daddy, I'm all right. But it was terrible. Just terrible."

He put his arm around me and held me close to him as we walked to the car. "Now tell me," he said, "tell me what happened."

I said, "It was that boy. That Elliot. He was drinking and, oh, he was just awful. I don't want to talk about it."

My father said, "God-damned that kid. Wait until I get my hands on him."

I said, "He asked me to go to the corner with him for some Seven-Up and then he just kept going. He had Helen's car."

"God-damned Helen," he said. "Where was she all this time?"

"I don't know," I said. "I saw her just to say hello and then she disappeared."

"She's going to hear about this." My father spoke through clenched teeth. "By God, she's going to hear about this."

When we were home, he took my coat off me and put it down in a chair. Then he led me over near the lamp and put his hands on my shoulders and looked at me and said, "Now, honey, don't be afraid to tell the truth. Did that boy harm you?"

I said, "No, Daddy, honestly he didn't. I got away from him. I pretended I was sick and I got the car locked and drove away from him."

"Thank God," my father said. "Thank the Lord for that."

He went to the phone then and in a moment I heard him say, "Helen, Jim. I'd like to know what the hell is going on over there."

Then, after listening a moment, he said, "She's here. She's all right. No thanks to you or that filthy young pup Harry brought home with him."

There was another pause and then he said, "I don't know where he is. But if I ever lay eyes on him again, he'll wish he'd never been born."

My father banged down the receiver and a thrill went through me. It was seldom he was ever angry at anyone. I had never heard him talk to anyone as he had to my aunt. Never had I felt so protected. I remembered the soft, cushioned feeling I'd had the day before my mother's funeral. Again I felt as though I were on velvet.

I said, "Helen's car is out at the Dineamite. I suppose we ought to tell her."

"Yes, I suppose so," he said, "but that can wait. Right now I'm going to get you to bed. You've been through enough for one evening."

That night he sat by my bed until I fell asleep. "Just forget the whole dirty business, honey," he said. "Just put it out of your mind and go to sleep."

Chapter 20

❧ ❧ ❧ ❧ ❧ ❧ ❧ ❧ ❧ ❧ ❧ ❧

The next morning my father and I slept late and my aunt showed up while we were eating breakfast. She charged into the kitchen, as sure of herself as ever.

"I came to tell you, Jim," she said, "that I sent that young man packing, bag and baggage, on the early train."

"Good riddance," my father said. "He'd better never show his face around this town again."

My aunt helped herself to coffee and sat down across the table from me. She said, "I can't tell you, Dorrie, how sorry I am about the whole miserable mess."

"I didn't like him from the beginning," I said. "He had a shifty look."

She stirred sugar into her coffee. "Well, I consider myself a pretty good judge of character, but I must say that boy pulled the wool over my eyes."

She sipped her coffee and put in more sugar. "Harry's just heartsick," she went on. "Elliot had him fooled too. Harry tried to defend Elliot, but I said, 'Now, Harry, you just listen to your mother. You're too trusting. Just because you're an honorable boy, you think all boys are. No real friend would treat your cousin the way this boy treated Dorrie.'" My aunt sighed. "Harry has such a strong sense of loyalty."

My father said, "What about his loyalty to Dorrie? I should think she'd come first."

"Yes," she said, "that's exactly what I told him."

• • •

That afternoon I seemed unusually tired and I thought it was from the previous night's excitement. Outside it was a gray, cold New Year's Day, but inside our house it was warm and cheerful. Anna and Mrs. Berkson were sitting at the kitchen table, talking and drinking coffee. My father and I were in the living room, both of us reading. The fire in the fireplace burned bright and warm, but I kept moving my chair closer to it. I kept feeling cold. Finally I gave up. I put away my book and got the afghan and lay down on the sofa.

The dream I had was terrifyingly real. My mother wasn't dead. She never had been. She had only been taking care of my grandma. Grandma was the only one who knew she was still alive.

My mother came into the house, laughing and calling out, "Yoo hoo, Jimmy, Dorrie, I'm home."

My father went to kiss her and he didn't seem to think it strange that she had a swimming suit on.

He said, "Annie, darling, you're back." He didn't seem to notice he'd called her Annie, either.

I woke up crying, and my father was bending over me, smoothing back my hair and saying, "There, there, baby, it was only a dream."

When I quieted down, he left the room and came back carrying a thermometer. "You feel awfully warm," he said.

He put the thermometer in my mouth and while we waited he said, "It's no wonder you had a nightmare after last night."

I had a little fever and he brought me aspirin. "I think you'd better go up to bed, baby," he said, but I said, "Please, Daddy, let me stay down here with you. I don't want to be alone."

The feeling of my mother's being in the house wouldn't go away. My father said, "All right, honey, you can stay down here." He tucked the afghan around me and said, "Try to sleep if you can. You're worn out after last night."

My father sat down in his chair and started reading again. The fire was pleasant and cheerful. I could hear Anna and Mrs. Berkson still in the kitchen. But then I thought, what if I only think it's Anna out there? What if there isn't any Anna at all?

I got up and my father said, "Did you decide to go to bed?"

I said, "No, I'll be right back."

It was Anna. It wasn't my mother. I ran a glass of water and stood at the sink, drinking it. But on my way out of the kitchen I brushed against Anna's shoulder. I had not only seen her; I had felt her. I knew she was real.

When I went back into the living room, I felt better and I didn't lie down again. I sat up, tucking the afghan around my knees. I knew it had been foolish of me to doubt that my mother was dead. Only my poor, old, confused grandma would do that.

I could remember every detail of the day my mother died. It was Friday and my father was taking the day off so we could have a three-day boating weekend. When I came downstairs that morning, my father had gone after bait and my mother was in the kitchen getting things ready. You'd have thought we were going to take a trip around the world. She had a list and she kept checking off things—the binoculars, the transistor radio, the alcohol stove, mosquito netting, and, of course, my bedroll. There was sleeping space for them in the cabin of the boat, but I had to sleep out on the deck.

I went to the refrigerator to get a piece of cheese, and my mother said, "Don't you want an egg and some toast?"

"No, thanks," I said. "Cheese is just what I want."

She was so busy that for once she didn't keep after me. I started to go out to the back yard, but she said, "Dorrie, why don't you invite Barbara Stuart to come with us. You girls could have a wonderful time. There'd be plenty of room for her to sleep on deck with you."

"Okay," I said in that spiritless way that drove her crazy. One of her theme songs was, "I can't understand why she doesn't want friends her own age."

I went into the den and dialed a number and put my hand down on the button. I pretended to talk to someone. Then I went back into the kitchen and told my mother Barbara didn't want to go.

"Well, isn't there someone else you'd like to invite?" she asked.

"Okay," I said, "I'll ask Sandy." I started for the den again. She said, "Oh, Dorrie, I do believe you like that girl just to torment me. You know how your father and I feel about her."

I turned back to the kitchen. "All right," I said, "if you don't like my friends, I'm sorry, but I can't help it."

She sighed and said, "Why, when I was your age, I had all kinds of friends."

Later, when we were getting into the car, my mother said, "Sit up front with us, honey," but I stayed in back where I knew she'd always wanted me.

Our boat was docked at one of the big marinas, and before we took her out, Daddy bought ice and beer and pop and put it in the cooler on deck.

That morning we cruised around, looking at the summer homes along the shore and noticing good islands for picnics. My parents never did any drinking in the mornings at home, but the sun was beating down and it was getting hot and my father said, "Well, I don't know about you, but I'm going to have a beer." They had their beer and I had pop, and then they had more beer and began to get a little gayer than usual, as they did at parties.

At noon we docked at a hamburger place that was sticking out into the water. We had hamburgers and potato chips and they went on drinking beer. A girl in a Bikini walked by our table and my father whistled at her. I despised my mother for the good-natured way she laughed.

When we had eaten, and while my father was getting gas, my mother looked in the cooler and said, "Jimmy, sweetie, the beer's getting low."

My father said, "That won't do," and he went back into the hamburger place and came out carrying a full case.

We left the dock and my father headed south. They were getting sillier all the time. They'd finish one can of beer, punch holes in it so it'd sink, toss it overboard, and open another right away. My head began to ache and I sat in one of the plastic chairs on deck and closed my eyes and tried not to hear them talking and laughing.

It must have been around two o'clock when my mother gave me a thought and she said, "Dorrie, you're so quiet, honey. Do you feel all right?"

"I'm perfectly all right," I said. "I'm just bored, that's all."

She said, "We can't have that. We can't have anyone bored on the good ship *Eleanore*. That's one of the rules. Right, Captain Jim?"

"Right," my father said.

My mother started taking the skis out of their slings and she said, "What you need, Dorrie, darling, is some stirring up. I prescribe some skiing for you."

It didn't surprise me at all that the first thought she had was to get me out of the boat. She was completely predictable.

I said, "No, I'm not going to ski."

My father said, "Dorrie, don't be so cross. Your mother's only trying to help you have a little fun."

My mother said, "That's all right, honey. If you don't want to ski, I'll ski. You be towrope man."

She adjusted the skis to fit her and my father slowed the boat. Then she threw them overboard. My father started to hand her a life belt, but she laughed and said, "I don't need that thing," and jumped into the water without it.

My father cut off the motor and leaned over the side of the

boat with the life belt and said, "Come on now, Eleanore, don't be ridiculous. Put this on."

She was laughing and struggling to get into the skis and she said, "Look, I'm a big girl now. Throw me the towrope."

For a moment my father held the life belt, then he tossed it under his seat and threw the rope to her. It fell short and he pulled it in and gave it another toss, and this time it came close and she caught it.

"Okay, Dorrie," he said to me, "you know the signals. Keep your eye on her."

I knew them well enough, the speed-up, slow-down, stop signals. My mother liked so much to show off that she used the speed-up signal more than any other.

My father started the motor, and we moved forward slowly until the line of the towrope was stretched straight out behind us. My mother lifted the bar to show there was no slack. My father yelled, "Ready?" and she yelled back, "Go."

We jumped ahead and she came up out of the water as though there were nothing to it. She skied far out to the right and then sped back across the wake to the left. Then she let herself ride directly behind us and gave me the speed-up signal. "Faster!" I yelled to my father, and over the roar of the motor I heard him yell, "Okay, faster."

We had been in the main channel where there were lots of other boats, but now he swung into a deserted cove and we went all around the edge of it. There was a terrible glare on the water and my head was pounding. I wished I had my sunglasses with me or that I could close my eyes. Just as we started to round the bend from the cove to the main channel, my mother lost her balance and fell. There were lots of boats and skiers in the channel and my father was busy steering, and I was tired of having my head hurt and I closed my eyes. It felt good to have my eyes closed.

When I opened them again, we were far out in the channel

and the towrope was skipping along the top of the water after us, and I yelled, "Stop, Daddy, stop."

Thinking about my mother that New Year's Day had made me feel worse and I said, "Daddy, I feel terrible. My throat hurts."

He came over and felt of my cheek and took my temperature again.

"It's up," he said. "I think I'll call Doc Moore."

When the doctor came, he looked at my throat and listened to my chest and said, "It's a virus that's going around now. I'll give you a prescription. She'll be good as new in a few days."

I only wish he had been right.

When the doctor left, my father went to the drugstore to get my medicine and Anna came into the living room to sit with me.

"Do you feel like eating anything?" she asked me. "Maybe a little soup?"

"I'm not hungry," I said, and she got a washcloth and wiped my face. Then she turned out the lamp and stayed with me until my father came back.

My father read the directions on the bottle and gave me my medicine and then he said, "I want to get you in bed now, honey," and we went upstairs with Anna coming along behind.

She came into my room with us and started unbuttoning my sweater. My father pulled down the blinds and turned back my bed and went out.

If I hadn't been so sick, I wouldn't have given in. I wouldn't have let her unbutton my sweater. I would have said, "No, thanks, Anna. You go on downstairs or to your room. My father and I will manage."

When I was in bed, my father came back and kissed me and turned out the duck lamp. I said, "Don't go, Daddy. Don't leave me alone."

He sat down beside my bed and the next thing I knew he was waking me up to give me my medicine. The night was a long mixed-up jumble. I didn't know when I was dreaming and when I was awake.

Chapter 21

ↀ ↀ ↀ ↀ ↀ ↀ ↀ ↀ ↀ
ↀ ↀ ↀ ↀ ↀ ↀ ↀ ↀ

When I woke up the next morning, I felt as though I'd been fighting a battle all night instead of sleeping.

Anna came into my room and smiled and said, "How are you feeling?"

"I'm tired," I said. "Where's Daddy?"

"He had to go to the office. He didn't want to waken you." She raised the blinds, but the glare from outside hurt my eyes and I asked her to lower them again.

At ten she gave me my medicine and made a note of it on a pad by my bed. I could see by the marks on the paper that my father had given me medicine three times during the night, but it seemed to me I had taken it ten or twelve times.

Anna wanted me to eat something, but I had no appetite. At twelve the mail came, and she brought a letter upstairs to me. I opened it and glanced at the signature. It was from Elliot Whelan. He had written:

Dear Dorrie,
You little liar. Boy, are you ever poison. Harry says you always were a sneak. I hope some day you get what's coming to you.
Elliot Whelan

For an instant I had a glimpse of how New Year's Eve looked to Elliot. But there had been no way of teaching my aunt and my father not to force me into dates without involving him.

The important thing was to get rid of the letter. I was shaky and weak, but I got up and put on my robe and went downstairs. Anna was in the kitchen. I went into the living room, took a match from the mantel, put the letter and envelope in the fireplace, and set fire to them. When they had curled into black shadows, I blew on them and the letter was gone. Except that I remembered it.

I wished that I could explain to Elliot that I had been forced into doing what I did, that I really had nothing against him. As I went back upstairs, I wished my father and I could move to a new town where there were no relatives or friends so I could start being good.

I climbed into bed, surprised at how weak I felt. I lay back, feeling as though I would never move again. I fell asleep. When I woke up, I was trying to push the water bugs away. I was sitting up, pushing the blanket and sheet to the foot of the bed. I lay back, uncovered, but I couldn't lie still. I twisted one way and another. Before long Anna came in, and although my room is small, she seemed very far away.

She pulled the blanket up over me and said, "Better stay covered, Dorrie. You'll catch more cold."

She took the thermometer out of the glass by my bed, looked at it, shook it down, and put it in my mouth. I couldn't keep my head still, even when she was taking my temperature.

Then she and my father and the doctor were all in the room. The doctor said something about changing my medicine, and his glasses glared at me and gave me a headache. The glare was terrible and the sun was hot. Just before I closed my eyes, my mother lurched and fell over in the water.

They kept putting warm, wet towels on me, wrapping them all around me, and then taking them off and putting them on again.

"Just let me alone," I said. "Please, please, just let me alone."

My mother said, "No, you've put it off long enough now, Dorrie. The recital is only three weeks away. You go right in there and practice."

But I fooled her. She didn't know how to read music and I played my old lesson over and over again. When the timer rang, she said, "All right, honey, your hour's up." The melody of the exercise I'd been playing last kept going through my mind. I tried to think of something else. I tried to remember the tune of another song. But there was just that melody, beating, beating, making my head hurt worse.

"Get it away, Daddy. Make it go away," I said.

But he didn't understand me and the room was dark and they had all gone and left me alone. That was when I heard the thumping on the stairs. I hardly breathed, hoping she would stop at her room, but she didn't, and I heard her bad foot dragging down the hall toward me. I wished I had thought to bring the bone-handled knife to my bed. I wished I had it hidden under the blanket in my hand.

She knocked at the door. I didn't answer.

She said, "Dorrie, I've got a little bedtime snack for you."

The door started to open and I screamed, "Daddy, Daddy, Daddy."

My father held me in his arms and said, "There, there, baby, it's all right. Daddy's here."

He stayed with me all night, never leaving me once. He brought the little lamp from the dressing table in his room and put it on the floor in the corner, and every time I opened my eyes he was sitting by my bed. Sometimes he gave me my medicine and sometimes he took my temperature. Every once in a while he gave me orange juice, and I drank all I could for him.

Once I opened my eyes and he was asleep in my rocker, his

head on one side. For a moment I didn't feel the headache or the sore throat or the pain in my chest. All I felt was how I loved him.

I dreamed I was lying in a tent. There were lots of people camping and my father was in charge. He had to find places for everyone to sleep. When he had everyone settled down for the night, he was going to come sleep with me. All the time I was sick, that was the only good dream I had.

For several days things were mixed up for me. I knew my father didn't go to work and I knew the doctor came several times, but they looked as though they were far away from me. Some nights Anna sat beside me and some nights my father did. I remember seeing Aunt Helen and the Stevensons and Mrs. Berkson. Finally I began to know the difference between what was happening and what I was dreaming.

One day the doctor looked in my throat and listened to my chest and as he put his stethoscope in his bag, he said, "She's better, Jim. Just keep her quiet and keep on with the medicine."

He looked at me then and said, "You've been a pretty sick young lady, did you know that, Dorrie?" He tweaked my nose in the way he had ever since I was little and said, "Now, just because you're feeling better, I don't want you to get rambunctious. You're not to get out of this bed until I say so, understand?"

"We'll keep her down," my father told him. "She's pretty feisty when she's well, but Anna and I together will be a match for her." He smiled at Anna then and said, "We'll manage, won't we?"

He shook hands with Dr. Moore and said, "I can't thank you for all you've done. You'll never know how I appreciate it."

The doctor left, and Anna and my father stood looking down at me and they both had the same pleased, happy expression on their faces.

My father moved my rocker a little and said, "Here, Annie, sit down. You've just about had it."

Anna still smiled at me and she said, "I'm all right. Everything's all right as long as Dorrie's better."

She sat in the rocker and I could see she looked thinner than usual and I wondered how much time she'd spent taking care of me. I noticed that my father called her Annie and I thought of Little Orphan Annie, but now it didn't fit. She and my father had been taking care of me together. They had been in something together. I had to hurry and get well.

I said, "Anna, I'm hungry. Could I have some soup?"

Anna got up, but my father said, "No, Annie, sit still. You were up last night. I don't want you down sick too. I'll get it," and he left the room.

I didn't like being indebted to Anna and I said, "Thank you for taking care of me when I was sick. When I get well, I'll buy you a present."

She gave a little laugh and said, "Honey, you know you don't have to do that. It's present enough that you're better."

I didn't like her calling me, "honey." I didn't like the way she was moving in close.

When my father came back, he was carrying the big tray. He had brought soup and sandwiches for all three of us. Anna brought a card table from the hall closet and they sat at it, and I sat up in bed with the tray on my lap.

Anna tasted her soup and smiled at my father and said, "You're a pretty good cook, Mr. Lawson."

My father laughed. "I'm a handy man with a can opener," he said.

My father finished eating and leaned back in his chair and looked at Anna and said, "We've really been through it, haven't we? We've been through the mill."

Anna smiled at me. "It was worth it. Did you know you gave us an awful scare?"

184 *The Velvet Bubble*

My father said, "That's right, baby, you sure did. I don't know what we'd have done without Annie."

I felt like saying that if we were totally dependent on Anna, it was something new, that ordinarily Aunt Helen and the Stevensons and Mrs. Berkson could be counted on to help us out. But I knew he was so happy to have me better that his gratitude to Anna was making him fond of her.

I felt too tired to worry about it. I said, "I don't want any more." Anna took my tray and I slid down in bed and closed my eyes.

My father came and kissed my forehead and said, "You rest now, baby."

They left my room, and just before I drifted to sleep, from downstairs there came the sound of my father's laugh.

Chapter 22

ᚽ ᚽ ᚽ ᚽ ᚽ ᚽ ᚽ ᚽ ᚽ ᚽ ᚽ ᚽ ᚽ

The next day was Monday, and my father went back to work. He peeked into my room that morning and saw that I was awake and came in and said, "How's my girl this morning?"

He was so handsome in his plain gray suit that I couldn't keep from thinking of Harry and Elliot in their silly uniforms. My father didn't need a uniform.

I said, "I feel better, Daddy. I wish you didn't have to go."

He said, "Someone's got to bring home the bacon. I'll tell you what, though, tonight when I come back, I'll bring my girl a present."

It was the first time he'd said "my girl" to me and I was glad I'd gotten sick. Not since my mother died had he called anyone that.

"For now, though," he said, "I want you to see something I ordered especially for you."

He went to his room and came back carrying two pillows. He helped me sit up and fluffed the pillows behind my back and said, "Now close your eyes."

In a moment he said, "Ready."

When I opened my eyes, he had raised the blinds and pushed back the curtains and I was looking out into a beautiful snowfall. Big lazy flakes drifted past my window.

"It's beautiful," I said. "When did you order it?"

He laughed and said, "Last night by Western Union."

When he had gone, I sat there watching the lovely snow he'd

given me, feeling warm and safe and contented. I thought of the sherry we'd had on New Year's Eve and of our toast to each other. I could still hear his voice saying, "my girl." I imagined his leaving the office after work, walking through the snow to buy a present for me. It was coming true. Gradually the bubble was beginning to surround us.

Before long Anna came in and helped me wash and then she brought my breakfast. While I ate, she sat in the rocker, looking out at the snow. "Poor Anna," I thought, "she has no one to order snow for her." I remembered the way I'd felt the night before about my father calling her Annie, but now it didn't bother me. The shadowy outlines of the bubble that were beginning to surround my father and me gave me such a feeling of safety that he could call her Annie and it was all right. I might even start calling her that myself.

After breakfast I slept a while, and when I woke up the snow was still falling, in smaller flakes, but faster than ever. Just before noon Mrs. Berkson came.

"I brought you some of my chicken broth, Dorrie," she said, and by the way she said it, I could tell she thought her chicken broth was something special. "I left it in the kitchen. Anna will bring it up later."

I said, "That's nice of you, Mrs. Berkson. Can you sit down for a while?"

She settled herself in my rocker. She said, "I was in and out while you were so sick. There didn't seem to be much I could do, though. I must say my heart went out to your father —the poor man was beside himself."

I said, "He stayed with me day and night. He stayed home from work to take care of me."

She said, "Yes, I know. He and Anna. I tell you that girl was a jewel. She couldn't have been better if you'd been her own kin."

"Anna's a hard worker," I said.

"Not only that," she said, "your own mother couldn't have done more. She was up and down those steps a hundred times a day and staying up nights too."

"My father and I appreciate it," I said. "We'll do something for her, a gift or a bonus or something."

Mrs. Berkson looked surprised, and I felt sure that she would rather we went on feeling indebted to Anna, just the way she wanted everyone forever thanking her for anything she'd done.

All of a sudden I felt sorry for her, with her good deeds and her kindnesses which she tried to trade for friendship. I felt so full of the happiness of the beginning bubble that I wanted to do something for her.

I said, "Mrs. Berkson, I've never forgotten the way you stayed with me when my mother died."

The smile she gave me was almost brilliant and she said, "Why, you know, honey, I wouldn't of had it any other way."

When she left the room a little later, I could almost see her carrying my remark with her, hugging it close.

That afternoon, after my nap, Anna came in and wanted to know if I'd like to have her read to me.

I said, "No, thanks, I think I'll just watch the snow."

I thought she would go to her room until time to cook dinner, but instead she sat down in my rocker.

"You know, Dorrie," she said, "on snowy days like this when I was a little girl, the farm was so far from the highway that I couldn't get to school. Sometimes my mother would make butterscotch candy, and we'd take part of it to the back porch and pour it on the snow. It would harden right away, in all kinds of shapes with long strings and curlicues." She smiled and added, "I used to think that was wonderful."

I could see by her face that she still thought it was wonderful. Just thinking about it made her look pretty. I remembered that the day I'd first seen her I'd thought that she could be nice looking if she wanted to. She didn't seem to expect an answer to what she'd said. She sat looking out at the snow and I sat looking at her. I realized it wasn't only the expression on her face that was making her look pretty. She was still wearing her hair cut in bangs the way I'd worn mine for a time, and the pale blue dress she wore was becoming. I wondered when she'd started wearing lipstick. I was almost sure she hadn't worn it at all when she first came to work for us.

"Do you have a boy friend, Anna?" I asked.

She laughed and said, "Whatever gave you that idea?"

I said, "I would think you would have—that you'd want one."

She looked more serious then and said, "I had a boy friend. I almost married him. But that was a long time ago. He and my father didn't get along, and finally I just gave up the idea."

I said, "Don't you get lonely, living here practically by yourself?"

She said, "No, not really. I like it here. You may not realize it, Dorrie, but the books you've given me to read have made all the difference in the world. I guess I got my liking for reading from my mother."

She was a real reader—not like Virginia Stevenson, always saying she wanted to read but that she didn't have time. Anna had read more books in the months she'd been with us than most people did in years. And she respected books and took care of them, the way I did. The thought flashed through my mind that, in spite of the difference in our ages, if things had been different, if the time or the place or something had been different, I would have loved to have her as my best friend. The glimpse into the friendship we might have had, but would never have, made me feel a little sad.

It was still snowing and darkness was coming on early. I said,

"Anna, would you hand me the make-up box from my bureau?"

She gave it to me and went downstairs to cook dinner, and I began to get ready for my father to come home. I had on the only bed jacket I owned, a white woolly one, and I wished it were prettier. As I combed my hair and put on lipstick, I noticed that I was still weak. My arms felt heavy, and when I finished, I was glad to sink back against the pillows.

When my father came home, he didn't even stop downstairs to take off his coat. He came into my room, with snow glistening on him, smelling like the outdoors.

He said, "Which hand do you want, baby?" And I chose the right, and I could see him transfer the package to his left, and then I said the left, and he laughed and handed me a white box with a red ribbon around it.

Inside was a beautiful soft pink wool scarf.

"Daddy, it's just beautiful," I said. I tied it over my head and reached for the make-up box on the bedside table. I remembered that Mrs. Mason had said pink was my color, and although I didn't like thinking about her, she had been right. I held my arms out and my father leaned down and I gave him a hug and a kiss.

My father went downstairs to fix his drink, and while he was gone, I thought of how he'd teased me with the present, putting it first in one hand and then in the other. That kind of teasing, loving and mischievous, was part of being in the bubble. The bubble was becoming less shadowy.

I think my father had only one drink that evening. I know that gradually, after I was sick, he started drinking less. He brought his glass to my room. When he had almost finished his drink, Anna came in, carrying the big tray with our dinner on it.

My father jumped up and said, "Here, let me take that. It's heavy. You should have called me."

Anna got the card table, and again the two of them sat at it and I ate in bed.

I wasn't very hungry, and soon I pushed my tray aside and took my scarf from its box. "Look, Anna," I said. "See what my father brought me."

She came to the bed and felt of the scarf and said, "It's beautiful, Dorrie. Such a lovely shade of pink."

Then in a playful way she said, "Did you know you're not the only one around here who got a present? I got a present, too, I'll have you know."

She left the room and came back carrying a book. It wasn't a book I'd have cared to own. I've never been interested in birds. But Anna was. My father had spent time finding a book she would like very much.

I held the book and pretended to look through it at the colored pictures and kept my voice pleasant when I said, "It's very nice."

But I wished so much that my father hadn't bought a present for her. It took away from my present. He had left his office and tramped through the snow looking for two presents, not just for mine. Two presents had come into the house with him. And hers could easily have taken more time to find than mine did. I looked at my scarf and it wasn't nearly so beautiful as I had thought. You could walk into almost any clothing store in town and pick one up.

"Did you know that pink is my color, Daddy?" I asked.

"Why, I guess so, baby," he said. "You seem to look good in any color."

I almost missed seeing what my father had written on the flyleaf of the book. I gave the pages a final flip and his handwriting caught my eye. "To Annie," he had written, "with deep appreciation. Jim Lawson."

I felt better then, knowing that my father had given her the book to thank her for helping me get well, but I wished he had waited until I could have chosen something for her. I would have liked to sign the card, "Jim and Dorrie Lawson."

When they were through eating, Anna put everything on the tray and started to pick it up. My father took it from her. He said, "I'll take it down."

"Are you coming back?" I asked him.

"Before long, honey," he said. "I'll come back and tuck you in."

I felt very tired, but I didn't want to be tired. I wanted to spend the evening with my father. When he came back, I asked him if we could play honeymoon bridge a while.

He said, "I'm afraid not, baby. You need your sleep, and I brought work home from the office."

Months later, when I thought I heard noises in the night, I thought of that evening. I fell asleep right away. When I woke up, I thought it was very late. From downstairs I could hear voices—Anna's and my father's. When I turned on my bedside lamp, I saw it was only a little after nine. But Anna usually spent evenings in her room. I wondered what they were finding to talk about. Just as I got up to go to the stairs to listen, Anna called, "Well, good night, then. See you in the morning." My father said, "Good night, Annie," and I heard Anna come up the stairs and go into her room and close the door.

Chapter 23

❧❧❧❧❧❧❧❧❧❧❧❧

For several days I had to stay in bed. During this time Anna was in and out of my room, bringing me fruit juice and food, changing my sheets and pillow cases, and seeing to it that I had my medicine on time. In addition to this, she came in for short periods to sit with me and talk. Sometimes I didn't mind this. One afternoon we started discussing *Wuthering Heights*, and the time went by so fast that before we knew it my father was home and Anna hadn't started dinner and I hadn't fixed my make-up or combed my hair. But the evenings and nights were beginning to make me uneasy.

The three of us ate dinner in my room, and afterward, Anna would go downstairs to load the dishes in the dishwasher. I would settle down to having an evening with my father, but every night it turned out that Anna was with us. It was my father who started it. He and I were getting ready to play bridge. He heard her coming up the stairs and he called out, "Hey, Annie, come play cards with us." She didn't know how to play, but my father seemed to enjoy teaching her and we played three-handed. After that first evening, at some time or other while we ate dinner, my father would mention the night's card game. He started keeping a running score from night to night. Anna was just learning and she didn't do very well, and I suppose it was amusing, but my father enjoyed it. Too much he laughed and teased her about it. She was beginning to think she belonged with us.

I was anxious to get stronger and be up and around and get things back to normal. One afternoon Dr. Moore came and examined me and said I could be up for a while that day and by the following Monday I'd be able to go back to school. I waited to dress until just before my father came home from work. When he got home, I was in the living room waiting for him, with his drink and his cigar ready.

"Well, what's this?" he said when he walked in. "This looks like old times." He gave me a hug and by his smile I could see how happy he was to have me downstairs.

Anna had built a fire, and my father and I sat in our regular places on either side of the fireplace while he read his paper and had his drink. Pretty soon she came in from the kitchen and wanted to know if I felt like eating in the dining room that evening.

I said, "Yes, Anna, we'll go back to the way things were before I got sick."

But we never did. I was never able to make my father see that we were all better off with Anna doing her work and then going to her room to read and leaving us to live our lives together. On the evenings when the three of us didn't play cards, he'd invite her to sit by the fire with us while we all read. And she never refused. I couldn't tell whether this was because of a lack of knowing what was right or if she just didn't care.

This went on for several weeks before I mentioned it to my father. February first was my grandma's birthday. We had taken her a present and spent the evening with her and on the way home I said, "Daddy, I know Anna was very good when I was sick and worked hard and helped take care of me, but I don't think we have to make her a member of the family because of it."

My father glanced at me and sounded surprised when he said, "Why, what do you mean, Dorrie?"

I said, "Well, like playing cards with her and having her sit in the living room with us and all that."

He said, "If I didn't know you better, honey, I'd almost think you were being snobbish."

I said, "It isn't that. It's just that she's *not* a member of the family and I don't see any reason to act as though she is."

For a minute my father didn't answer me, and when he did, he said, "I thought we'd all been happier lately. God knows I have."

I said, "But, Daddy, don't you see, we started getting happier before I got sick. Don't you remember New Year's Eve?" I could tell by the way he said, "I remember," that he didn't remember our toast in the happy way I did. It hadn't meant the same thing to him that it did to me. But it had meant something. I knew it had. It couldn't have meant nothing. The snow he gave me, his calling me "my girl," all of that couldn't have meant nothing. I had begun to feel the bubble and I hadn't been wrong.

My father said, "I thought you and Anna were fond of each other."

I said, "It's not that. She's all right. But she's not my mother or my sister or my cousin. She's the housekeeper."

He said, "I don't like this, Dorrie—this wanting to put her in her place. She's a wonderful girl and she's been wonderful to us, and I'm not going to have her put down."

I didn't say anything more. She had moved in closer than I'd dreamed. The moment I got sick she took advantage. I'd made a mistake to mention it to my father. I should have worked quietly, the way she had, not letting him know what I was doing.

A few days later when I came home from school, Anna, as usual, had hot chocolate waiting for me. She poured two cups and we sat on either side of the kitchen table. My father had a dinner meeting that night and wouldn't be home until late.

"How was school today?" she asked.

"Fine," I said. Then I went on. "Anna, I've been thinking. You've been awfully good to me. I guess you know we're friends."

"Why, yes, Dorrie," she said. She smiled at me. "We hit it off right away, both of us liking to read so much."

I said, "Well, something's been on my mind. Something I think I ought to tell you. Something someone said."

She looked serious then. "About me?" she asked.

"Yes," I said. "I hardly know how to put it. But you know how people talk."

Her voice was very quiet. "What was it, Dorrie?" she asked.

I said, "I can't tell you where it came from."

"Just tell me," she said.

I said, "I know there's nothing to it, but they're saying you're too fond of my father, that you're throwing yourself at him."

I had never seen her angry. Her eyes flashed and she clenched her fists and she said, "Who said such a thing?"

I said, "I told you, I can't tell. I promised."

She jumped up from the table. "Of all the dirty lies," she said.

"They wouldn't dare say it to my face or to his."

"I haven't told him," I said. "I don't think we should worry him with it. I thought you'd want to know yourself, that you'd want to handle it yourself."

"How can I," she asked, "when they won't come out in the open, when they sneak behind my back and worry you with it?"

I said, "I thought you'd figure out what to do."

She said, "What do you mean, do you think I should leave, try to find another job?"

I said, "We'd miss you," I waited a moment and then I said, "But of course you have to think of yourself, of your reputation."

She started to leave the kitchen, not even rinsing out her

dirty cup, and I knew how upset she was. In the doorway she stopped and looked back at me. "Thanks for telling me, honey," she said. "It was the right thing to do."

She went up to her room and I wondered if she were packing. I rinsed out the cups and put them into the dishwasher. Then I went into the living room and put another log on the fire and sat watching it before I went upstairs to change my clothes. As I went past her room, I heard something. When I stopped to listen, I knew she was crying.

I have wondered many times what she planned to do, whether or not she was packing as I stood outside and listened. Everything might have been different if my father had gone to the meeting as he planned that night. Of if I had stayed downstairs and had been there when he came in. But I went on to my room, and in only a few minutes I heard him on the stairs. I went to my door to listen. He stopped outside her door and everything was quiet. Then he called, "Annie, what's the matter? What's wrong?"

There was silence and he said, "Annie, answer me. What's wrong?"

Still she didn't answer him, and he came down the hall toward my room. I moved over to my dresser and started brushing my hair.

He came in and said, "Hi, honey. Say, do you know what's wrong with Annie? She seems to be crying."

I was slow in answering him. Finally I said, "She's kind of moody. She never wants to talk about these spells."

He looked puzzled. He said, "I would have thought she wasn't moody at all. She seems very even tempered."

I said, "She hasn't wanted you to know. She does a good job of covering up."

He sat down in my rocker, his chin in his hand, looking out the window. "Are you sure nothing's happened?" he asked.

I said, "I was in school all day. Something might have happened. I doubt it. This is just the way she is."

I put down the hairbrush and said, "Let's go on downstairs. I think she wants to be let alone."

When we went past her room, there was no sound. She had stopped crying. Because I'd thought he wouldn't be home, I didn't have the drink tray ready and my father went into the kitchen and got the scotch. I went out and brought in the paper and put it by his chair. But he didn't read it. He picked it up, then put it down again. He stood up and walked around the room and then stood in front of the fireplace looking into the fire.

I said, "Really, Daddy, it's nothing to worry about. I think if you mentioned it to her, she'd be embarrassed."

He said, "I don't understand it. It doesn't seem like her."

At five o'clock she hadn't come downstairs and I said, "I believe I'll fix dinner. I can take a tray up to Anna."

He said, "Yes, honey, that's a good idea. It might make her feel better."

When I knocked on her door, she didn't invite me in. She took the tray and said, "Thanks, Dorrie. I was just coming down."

I said, "You've had a shock. You'd better rest."

She said, "Yes, I would like to be alone. Thanks, honey."

I said, "Anna, I've been thinking. Maybe I shouldn't have told you that. I hope you won't tell my father. He might be mad at me."

She said, "I won't tell him. I don't want to make trouble. But, Dorrie, tell me one thing. Was it Mrs. Berkson?"

"No, not Mrs. Berkson," I said.

She said, "I'm glad. I felt she was my friend and that would have hurt more."

Downstairs, my father asked, "How does she seem to be?"

"She's calming down," I said.

My father was quiet while we ate, and I realized more than I had before that in the past few weeks we'd had more talking and laughing in our house than we'd had since my mother died. I was on edge, wondering what Anna would do, wondering if I could trust her not to tell my father. If she did, he'd want to know where I heard the gossip. He knew I'd lied to the Stevensons. I couldn't bear to have him think I really was a liar. I was afraid he wouldn't understand that I only lied when I had to, that when I was finally in the bubble with him there would never again be any need to lie.

When I had put the dishes in the dishwasher and had cleaned up the kitchen, I asked my father if he'd like to play cards.

He said, "I don't think so, baby. I'm bushed. I'm going to bed before long."

I decided to do my algebra instead of waiting for study hall the next day. I sat at the gate-legged table and worked. Whenever I glanced at my father, he was just sitting there, not reading, not even smoking his cigar, and I wondered if he were thinking of Anna.

I had only one problem left when my father said, "I believe I'll go up, honey. Are you almost through?"

I stood up and put my arms around him and kissed him good night. "Yes," I said, "I'll be up in a few minutes."

But I didn't work the last problem. When my father went up the stairs, he tapped on Anna's door and called her name. And then, although I couldn't tell what they were saying, I heard their voices. I sat and listened and thought that in a minute my father would go on to his room. When he didn't, I put my books together and turned out the lights and went up the stairs. The door of Anna's room was open. She was sitting on the bed, my father on the straight chair near her window. My father was talking and I heard the end of a sentence,

". . . needs you so much." He looked up and saw me then and gave me a faint smile and didn't say anything. It was obvious he was waiting for me to pass by before he went on.

I stepped inside Anna's room and said to her, "Are you feeling better?"

She said that she was, and I was going to sit on the bed beside her until my father left, but he said, "You go on to bed now, honey. Tomorrow's a school day."

As I walked down the hall toward my room, I felt exactly as I had years before when my mother would say something like, "When we get her to bed, let's see if the Stevensons want to come over," and I was put to bed, banished, left out.

When I got in bed, I left the door to my room open, waiting to hear my father come down the hall. Their voices went on and on and I wanted desperately to hear what they were saying. Once I got up and stood in my doorway just out of sight, but I couldn't catch more than a word now and then. I thought that hours had passed and I took my clock into the bathroom to see the time. I could hardly believe it was only ten o'clock and that I'd been in bed less than an hour.

In a little while my father came down the hall and went into his room. I was awake for hours after that. The only sound was the wind outside and the ticking of my clock by my bed.

When I fell asleep, it was the old dream—I was walking down the street with my father. Then I was going to fall into the pit and my father was gone.

Chapter 24

The next morning Anna was her usual self. I did notice, though, that in spite of the fact that it was Friday, she had gone out of her way to cook sausage and waffles, which was ordinarily our Sunday breakfast.

I said, "Are we celebrating something?"

She laughed and said, "No, I'm making up for playing hookey at dinner last night."

That afternoon after school, when she and I were drinking our hot chocolate, she said, "I wanted to tell you, honey, that everything's all right."

I said, "What do you mean?"

She said, "You know that silly thing someone said—well, I'm not going to let it bother me."

She took a sip of her chocolate, then she went on. "You know, Dorrie," she said, "all we can do is our best. If we know in our own hearts that what we are doing is right, then nothing else matters."

I said, "You don't mind people talking?"

She said, "I don't think they are—not the people who count. There's always someone who will throw a little mud. But the reason they do is that they live in it. It's all around them."

I said, "You're not going to leave—you're staying with us?"

She said, "Yes, honey, you can count on it. Just forget the whole thing. Don't let it worry you."

I said, "Did you tell my father what I told you?"

She looked surprised. "Oh no," she said. "Don't you remember? I said I wouldn't."

I said, "Well, what did you tell him? I mean, you talked a long time last night."

"Yes," she said. "He knew I was upset, of course. He'd heard me crying. At first I didn't know what to tell him. Finally I just said that I got lonely sometimes—that sometimes I felt like trying to get a job where I'd be seeing people more. I had to tell him something."

I looked out the window at the dreary February afternoon. "I guess he wanted you to stay," I said.

She smiled. "Oh yes, he was very nice."

I couldn't figure out whether she was very stupid or very clever. She had played on my father's sympathies—telling him she was lonely. Had she done it deliberately or had she told him this only to keep from telling him what I'd said to her? It was hard to believe that she felt any such loyalty to me. Why should she?

I started watching her more closely than ever, trying to figure her out. She continued to act as if she thought she were a member of the family, asking me about my schoolwork, staying in the living room with us evenings, playing cards with us sometimes.

One evening the Stevensons dropped in unexpectedly. I was at the gate-legged table doing my homework, and Anna and my father were by the fire, reading. After she had said hello to them, Anna started to go to her room, but my father called her back.

It hurt me to see the smile he gave her. He said, "Where do you think you're going? Don't think you can sneak out like that."

He looked at Virginia then and said, "She's afraid she'll have to play cards with us and we'll beat her."

Virginia said, "I don't believe that for a minute. Come on,

　　　　　　　　　　　　　　　　　　　　　　　　　The Velvet Bubble

Anna, you and I will stand these two supermen and we'll show them who can play cards around here."

Right in front of me then they set up a card table. Once in a while one of them said something to me, but I had the feeling they were doing it the way you might throw bones to a dog. I didn't count. I was on the side lines, left out, the child doing homework.

My father fixed drinks, and when he asked Anna what she wanted, she said, "Oh, a coke, I guess."

He said, "Come on now, what kind of nonsense is that?"

She let him talk her into having a beer, and again I couldn't tell whether she really had never done any drinking or if it were an act she was putting on. Did she think such innocence would endear her to him?

She sipped the beer and said, "Well, I can't say much for the taste."

My father said, "You'll develop a liking for it."

My father had given me a Seven-Up, but I couldn't bear to stay in the room with them and I got up and said good night. I kissed my father's cheek and put my arm around his shoulder. He said, "Good night, baby. Your play, Dan."

Anna said, "Good night, honey."

"Good night, Anna," I said, and for a moment I stood looking at her, taking in the picture of her sitting at the card table next to my father. Her cheeks were a little flushed and her eyes were bright and happy. There was something shining about her. She wasn't the same person we'd seen that first day at the farm. She wasn't the outsider that I had decided could keep house for us.

As I went up to my room, that picture of her stayed in my mind. I lay in bed seeing it. I lay in bed hating it. I began to know how much I hated her, and from that night on the hate grew. I lay there seeing the picture and hearing the sound of their talking and once in a while the ringing out of my father's wonderful laugh. And then I had something sharp in my hand, and over and over I was plunging it into her. Even when she slipped over sideways in her chair and fell to the floor, I kept stabbing her.

I think I was awake almost all night. The Stevensons left around eleven, and Anna and my father came up the stairs together. I heard him say, "Good night, Annie," and go into his room and close the door. I heard the sound of my father's shower, and soon after that the house grew quiet. There was nothing to keep me awake except the hate inside me.

The night was long and I got up several times and looked at my clock. The last time I looked it was three o'clock and I put on my robe and sat in my rocker looking out at the street light below. Before long I got cold, and when I went to bed I fell asleep at last. Many nights after that I couldn't sleep. Even when nothing particular had happened the previous day to upset me, the hate stayed with me and kept me from sleeping. And then a night would come when I'd be so worn out that I'd fall asleep right away and sleep until morning. But I'd wake up with the uneasy feeling that there had been noises in the night and that I had missed them.

Through the early part of the spring things stayed about the same, except that I became more desperate all the time. My father liked Anna and wanted her with us whenever possible. The shadowy feeling of the bubble that I'd had when I was sick was gone.

The week before Easter I told Anna that I was going to have a four-day vacation from school and asked if she didn't want to go home during that time.

She said, "I don't believe so, Dorrie. Thanks anyway. My Christmas visit seemed to go on forever. There's really nothing for me there any more."

I said, "I imagine my father and I will be at my aunt's for Easter. We've always had Easter dinner with her."

She said, "Don't worry about me. I'll be all right."

Aunt Helen did invite us, and in the afternoon, after we'd eaten, my father left the house to buy cigars. My aunt and I were in the kitchen, doing dishes.

I said, "Helen, I'm worried about my father."

She said, "Oh? In what way? I thought he seemed happier and looked better than any time since Eleanore died."

I said, "Yes, he is happy, but not for a good reason."

She stopped washing dishes and looked at me. "What do you mean?" she said.

I said, "It's Anna. She's after him—doing everything she can to get him."

"And he likes her?" my aunt asked.

"Yes," I said. "Too much. He spends as much time as he can with her—playing cards, keeping her in the living room with us, having her help entertain our friends."

My aunt wiped her hands and sat down at the kitchen table. For a moment she didn't say anything. Then she said, "It hurts, I won't deny it. Eleanore's been gone such a short time."

I felt happier than I had in weeks. I thought, together we can lick Anna. Together my aunt and I can do it.

I said, "What are we going to do? How can we get rid of her?"

She gave me a sad smile and then she said, "I'm not sure we should do anything, Dorrie. I know how you feel. I feel the same way. You're thinking of your mother and you don't want anyone to take her place. But, honey," she went on, "he's got to go on living. He's been so lonely, so lost, since your mother died. Maybe we should be glad he's found someone."

"You can't mean that," I cried. "He doesn't need anyone. We don't need anyone. Can't you see that? My father and I don't need anyone."

"Maybe you don't now, Dorrie," she said. "The time will

come when you will, and then you'll understand why your father needs Anna."

"I'll never need anyone but my father," I said. "You don't understand. You just don't understand."

"Try to look at it this way," she said. "He was bound to find someone sooner or later. Try to be glad it's a fine person like Anna." She gave a little laugh then and went back to the dishes.

"Anyway," she said, "I don't think we need to rush out and buy wedding presents. Liking to have her around isn't marrying her, you know."

No, I thought, and it's not going to be. I didn't know what I would do, but I did know Anna wasn't going to have my father. Even if my aunt wouldn't help me, somehow or other I'd get rid of Anna. It wasn't too late. He wasn't in love with her; he only liked her. At one time I had wondered if Anna were very stupid or very clever. I knew now that she was very clever. And I would be just as clever as she. I wouldn't rush into anything the way I had when I'd talked to my father about her. I'd wait my time. My chance would come. And when it did, I'd be prepared, and before she knew it, she'd be out of the house and out of our lives for good. From that time on I played her game completely. Night after night Anna stayed with us in the living room. When it was my bedtime, I'd say good night to them and go upstairs, never letting on how I felt. I'd lie awake then, listening, and even after they were in their rooms, I often didn't sleep. Many times I sat in my rocker. I had waited a long time to get rid of my mother, and when I had, she was gone for good. I could wait to get rid of Anna too.

In the daytime I did little things against her, but I knew, even while I was doing them, that all they did was make me feel better for a short while. One day she had an apple pie in the oven. My father wasn't home yet, and I was checking my history notebook to hand in the next day. She came into the living room and told me she was going to run over to Mrs. Berkson's for a few minutes. As soon as she left, I went into the kitchen and turned the oven up to 550 degrees. As usual, her few minutes changed into half an hour. I sat at the kitchen table watching for her, and when I saw her coming, I turned the oven down again. By that time the air was filled with the smell of burned apple pie. She had to throw the whole thing away. The next day she had a man come to check the regulator, and when he found nothing wrong, she said, "I can't understand it. I'm sure I was right on my timing."

Sometimes, when she was gone, I'd go into her room to see what I could do. Once there were six stockings hanging in her bathroom, drying, and I took one of them and wadded it up in my hand and went down to the fireplace and watched it burn. I don't know what she thought. She never said anything about it.

I started telephoning her too. Every few days, from school, or the drugstore, or from Sandy's house, I'd dial our number, and when she answered I held my hand over the mouthpiece and just listened. Sometimes I dialed our number from our own house and hung up quickly. At first she wasn't bothered. But gradually she began to be more annoyed. "Hello, hello," she'd say, and one day she said, "Well, I hope you're enjoying this, whoever you are. I'm certainly not," and she banged down the receiver.

That night while we were eating dinner she told my father and me about it. She said, "At first I laughed it off, but now, I'll admit, it's getting under my skin."

My father said, "It's some crackpot. The world's full of them. If it keeps up, we can get an unlisted number."

Gradually after that I stopped calling her. I didn't want my father to have to go to the bother of telling everyone a new number.

.   .   .

It was in late April that I saw the cigar. Anna had started having her hair done once a week at a beauty shop, and I knew that on Wednesdays she wouldn't be home until four-thirty. I had gone into her room to look through her drawers. They were neat and orderly and not interesting. I was just going to leave when something caught my attention. At first I didn't know what. I stood in the middle of the room and then I knew I smelled a dead cigar. It was in the wastebasket and it was my father's brand. Could Anna be smoking my father's cigars? I tried to picture her with a cigar in her mouth. I really wanted to. But I couldn't. She didn't even smoke cigarettes.

But I could picture my father sitting there in her room, smoking a cigar. I could see him sitting on her straight chair and the two of them talking and laughing and enjoying themselves. I stood there in the room, remembering that the nights when I slept soundly all night I often woke the next morning with the feeling that there had been noises that I'd missed.

Chapter 25

Through spring the weather was beautiful. The grass turned green, and the cottonwood tree leafed out and the sun shone. But I only saw the beauty, I didn't feel it.

Anna did the spring house cleaning, washing windows, cleaning closets, scrubbing cupboards. On Saturdays my father worked in the yard. He put on his old gabardine pants and went around, whistling and getting things ready for summer. He pruned the roses and painted the screens and put them up and dug a small plot for an herb garden.

The more beautiful the weather, and the happier my father was, the worse I felt. I knew that the weather alone couldn't make him happy. We'd had many beautiful fall days after my mother died, but he had done no whistling.

Just before Memorial Day I saw artificial wreaths in the store windows, and that night I said to my father, "You don't go out to the cemetery any more."

He said, "That's right, Dorrie, I don't. Do you remember, honey, you told me once she wasn't there, that she was gone? I guess I finally realized it."

I said, "You still have the wedding picture on your bureau."

He looked surprised and said, "That's different. Just because she's gone doesn't mean I've forgotten her. I never will, you know that, no more than you will."

Daddy, Daddy, I wanted to cry, don't you see how mixed

up Anna is making you? Don't you see what she's doing to us?

My father gave me a look that was kind and sad at the same time. "What's wrong, baby?" he asked. He came and put his hand at the side of my cheek and said, "Is there something you can tell me about?"

"No, Daddy," I said, "I can't tell you. You wouldn't understand."

He sighed and said, "I know you miss your mother. A girl needs a mother to talk to."

Early that evening when the three of us were in the living room, my father got up and went to his room. When Anna started talking, I knew he'd said something to her.

She said, "Dorrie, is something bothering you? Something you'd like to talk to me about?"

"Hardly," I said. I made my voice as cold as I could.

"I was a girl once, you know," she said. "I just might understand better than you think I would."

"Anna," I said, "I know the facts of life, if that's what you're thinking of."

She said, "Why, no, I wasn't particularly thinking of that. There can be other problems."

I said, "I'm going over to see Sandy."

I started to leave the room, but she said, "Just a minute, Dorrie. Wait just a minute."

I stood looking at her, wondering if my eyes showed how much I hated her.

She looked a little embarrassed, but the softened expression of her face showed no awareness of my feelings.

Half jokingly, but serious, too, she said, "I've noticed something about us, Dorrie, about you and me."

I felt like saying, I've been doing some noticing, too, Anna, you dirty bitch.

I didn't ask the question she was waiting for and she went

on. "We're an awfully lot alike, did you know that, honey?"

That was so ridiculous that then I did ask the question. "In what way?" I said.

"Well, of course, there's the reading. But that's not the important thing." She laced her fingers together and looked down at her hands. "But we're not like most people—we keep things to ourselves. We don't do much talking about our problems. I guess I started being like this when my mother died."

"Just what problems do you think I have?" I asked her.

She gave a little shrug. "I've no idea. All I know is that I'd like to help if I can."

What I saw next was so astonishing I could hardly believe my eyes. She started to smile—she wanted to smile—but a grimace of something close to sorrow distorted her expression and she said, "Did you know you're very dear to me?"

I knew then that, as much as she liked my father, she liked me too. But I knew *like* wasn't the word—not for the way she had spoken and the expression I'd seen on her face. If I had never known my father, if he had died before I was born, if I'd had to grow up only knowing other people, I wouldn't have been able to recognize the fact that in some way Anna had started loving me. What I had seen on her face and heard in her voice was something like what I felt for my father.

"I guess I won't go to Sandy's right now," I said. "I have a headache. I'm going to lie down."

She didn't answer, and I knew she'd expected me to say something else. I went upstairs and closed the door of my room and lay on my bed. A gentle breeze moved my curtains and outside birds were singing. I didn't know what to think or how to feel. I saw the expression on Anna's face and heard her words again, and I knew she hadn't been pretending. Because of my love for my father, I knew how love felt.

But it didn't make sense. There was no reason for her to

love me. I didn't even want her to. I got up and sat in my rocker near the window. Later the street lights came on and cars went by, filled with families enjoying the early-summer night. But I couldn't enjoy the nice breeze or the freedom of vacation. I felt confused. I was bewildered by the contrast of my hate for Anna and her affection for me.

She wasn't seeing at all the way I felt about her. It was true, I'd tried to hide my feelings. I hadn't wanted her to know I was waiting for the chance to get rid of her. I hadn't wanted her to be on guard. But it was hard to believe that she thought I liked her, that she thought affection from her would be welcome to me.

Then, in a flash, like suddenly seeing the solution to an algebra problem, I saw what she had been doing. She hadn't been seeing me. She hadn't been seeing me any more than people other than me saw my father. No doubt she knew that my hair was dark and my eyes were brown and that I was slender and medium height, but she had seen only the surface. She had seen that I gave her books to read and that for a long time I'd made a point of speaking to her kindly and that I had taught her how to get used to doing things our way. My real feelings, which I knew came through often lately, she had ignored. She hadn't wanted to see them.

She wanted to think things were all right between us. Because in that way she felt free to love me. The key, of course, was my father, as I might have known. He would see she loved me, and that would draw him closer to her.

I wasn't confused any longer. I left my room. As I walked down the hall, I heard the sound of my father's shaver and I wondered if he had some kind of a meeting that night. Usually he shaved only in the morning.

But he had no meeting. Anna was in the kitchen, putting ice cubes in the ice pail. She asked me if I felt better and I said I did. She said, "That's good. The Stevensons are coming over. Your father and I thought it would be fun for all of us to drive out later and see the new swimming pool."

I said, "I didn't know we had plans. I didn't know the Stevensons were coming. Did they call?"

"No," she said. "Your father called them."

But he hadn't bothered to tell me. He'd told Anna, and it was Anna who was getting ready to entertain them. I noticed that while I'd been in my room, she'd changed her clothes. I said, "Anna, isn't that a new dress?"

"Yes," she said. "Do you like it?" She seemed to be delighted that I'd noticed.

I said, "It seems a little dressy," and watched the smile fade from her face.

When the Stevensons came, Anna and my father and I were in the sun porch. I watched everyone carefully. It was hard to believe that none of them caught the irony of the scene. The Stevensons, loyal friends of my parents for so many years, abject admirers of my mother, were accepting completely and even joyfully the idea that my father and Anna were a couple. They'd never done that for me. When I had done my best, been most adult, looked my nicest, they'd never accepted my father and me as a couple. They'd sat around and talked about my mother. But no one was talking about my mother this evening. Not until I started.

"Anna," Virginia said, "isn't that a new dress? It's very pretty."

Anna said, "Thanks." She glanced quickly at me and added, "It may be a little dressy."

"Oh no." Virginia's tone was flattering. "It's very becoming. I've never seen you looking prettier."

The look my father gave Anna was one he'd often given my mother. "I'm proud of you," it said. He'd always liked to have the Stevensons brag on my mother and now he liked having Virginia brag on Anna.

I said, "My mother had a dress that same shade of lavender. It was a summer dress, made of voile with white lace around the neck. Do you remember, Virginia? Do you re-member?"

They were all looking at me, and I realized that, although I'd started speaking in a normal tone, my voice had become louder and higher as I went on.

I lowered my voice and said, "Do you remember, Daddy? Do you remember my mother in that dress?"

My father looked at me tenderly. "I remember, honey," he said.

Virginia came to the chair where I sat and rubbed her hand down the back of my hair and said quietly, "We'll never forget your mother, Dorrie. You know that, don't you?"

I think I would have been all right if Anna had kept quiet. "We never forget the people who have been dear to us," she said.

I saw the way my father looked at her. There was the tender-ness with which he had looked at me. But there was something more. She looked at him and there was something between them. There was something I'd never had. Not really, not fully. I forgot the Stevensons were there. They didn't matter.

All that mattered was the bubble around Anna and my father.

Something started growing in me. It got bigger and bigger and louder and louder. I knew I had to get out of there. I stood up and started across the room. But it was too big, too loud. I couldn't stand it and I started screaming.

"I hate her, I hate her," I screamed. I could hear my voice filling the room, filling the house. I couldn't see or feel. All of me was in the screaming.

Chapter 26

❧❧❧❧❧❧❧❧❧❧❧❧❧❧❧❧

I never have been able to remember it, but I know they had the doctor come and give me some kind of a shot to calm me down. It made me sleep all night, a dreamless, dark, black sleep that I wasn't used to. When I woke up, I thought that it had been like dying. I thought of my dead mother, down in the black earth, sleeping the dreamless sleep. Blackness was all around me. Blankness and blackness. Outside the bubble everything was black. It always had been. Outside the bubble there was nothing.

My father came in, looking worried and tired.

"How are you feeling, honey?" he asked me.

"All right," I said. I couldn't explain the blackness to him. I couldn't explain it to anyone.

From my bureau he took a bottle of pills. "The doctor wants you to take these," he said, "for a while, until you feel better."

He went into the bathroom and came back with a glass of water.

"What are they?" I asked.

"I think some kind of tranquilizer. Just to get you over this little upset." He handed me the glass and I swallowed the bright orange pill.

He sat down on my bed then and put his hand on my knee. "What's bothering you, Dorrie?" he asked. "Is it Anna? Is it Anna you meant that you hated?"

I thought this was my chance, my one chance. I could see by

his face that it was me he was thinking of. He was worried about me.

I said, "I don't want her here, Daddy. I don't like what she's done here. She's ruining us. She's ruining our family."

"Dorrie, Dorrie," he said, and I waited, but he didn't go on. He sat there, looking at the floor, as though he didn't know what to do.

After a while he stood up. "We'll talk about it later, honey," he said. "Somehow we'll work things out. I've got to get to the office now."

He kissed me good-by and left and everything was quiet in the house.

It was much later when I went downstairs. Anna seemed to be gone and I went to the refrigerator and got myself a piece of cheese. Then, eating it as I went, I looked all over for her. She wasn't in any of the downstairs rooms or in the yard. Her door had been closed, and I went back up the stairs. When I tapped on her door there was no answer and I tapped again. "Anna," I called. Still there was silence.

Slowly I turned the knob on her door and pushed it open. She was sitting on the bed, looking trapped and unhappy. How could she be unhappy when she was in the bubble? I knew she couldn't be and that she had put on that look to make me feel sorry for her.

I went into her room and stood by the window, looking at her.

"You're not fooling me," I said.

She was a wonderful liar. "Dorrie," she said, "I've never tried to."

I laughed. I started laughing and I couldn't stop. I laughed and laughed, and I thought of Miss Blake and my father and Bobby Rollins tripping on his robe and almost dropping his present for the baby Jesus. It was all so funny. I could see now how funny it all was. And then, without any warning, my laughing turned to crying and I sank down in the chair by her window.

"Dorrie, Dorrie," she said, almost exactly the way my father had said it earlier.

"Don't be so unhappy, honey," she said, went on. "No one wants to hurt you. That's the last thing in the world anyone wants."

As fast as they had started, my tears stopped and I could feel the anger and the hate still strong in me. The doctor's shot and his stupid orange pills couldn't stop the way I felt. I knew again what I had always known, that no one can control the way you feel.

I clenched my fists and I pounded on the bed. "You're getting out of this house, do you understand?" I said. "You dirty bitch, you're not worthy to tie my father's shoestrings."

She moved back as though I'd hit her, her face white and drawn.

"Get out," I said. "Get out before it's too late."

There was silence then in the room, but not in me. I could hear the sounds getting louder and louder the way they had the night before.

"Dorrie," she said, "there's something you don't understand." I waited. I said nothing. I sat and listened to the sounds getting louder.

She said, "I love your father. I love him very much, but I love you, too, Dorrie. Please try to understand. I don't want to take anything away from you. I wouldn't hurt you for the world."

She stretched out her hand toward me, and with my clenched fist I knocked it away.

She put her hands over her face then and started crying. But the sounds in me were louder than her crying, and I stood up and grabbed her hair and yanked her head back. Then through clenched teeth, and slowly, so she would understand, I said, "You get out of this house. If you know what's good for you, start packing,"

I turned and left her room and I wished there were something I could hit and hit and hit over and over again.

I went downstairs, not knowing what I would do, only knowing the sounds I heard wouldn't let me keep still.

Stupid, stupid, self-righteous Mrs. Berkson was knocking on the back screen door.

She said, "Hi, honey, I brought you some of my first lettuce. Is Anna here?"

I said, "Mrs. Berkson, we don't want your lettuce or your chicken soup or you. Did you know you're the laughingstock of the whole town, going around doing things for people that they don't want you to do? Everyone's sick of the sight of you."

I liked seeing the way she got a little smaller, a little wilted down. I watched her walk across our lawn and across the alley and go in her back door and I wished I could have hurt her more. I wanted to hurt everyone. I thought of all the people I hated—Mrs. Berkson and my aunt Helen and Virginia and Dan and Mrs. Mason. But most of all Anna and my mother. They were together, the same person. My mother wasn't dead. She was there. As long as Anna was there, she was there.

All day long the anger and the hate were high in me. I was restless and couldn't settle down to doing anything. I couldn't read or sleep or write poetry or clean the house. Anna stayed in her room, and the house was mine to clean if I could have, and I took out the dustcloth and tried to dust my father's den, but I had to stop. I went to the phone and dialed Sandy's number and let it ring twice. In only a few minutes she was at the door and I was sorry I'd called her.

I said, "I shouldn't have called you, Sandy. I'm sorry I did. I can't talk now."

In her wonderful way, not understanding, but accepting, she said, "That's all right, Dorrie. See you later."

"See you," I said.

But I never saw her again.

The day was a year long, at least, at least as long as the time my mother had been dead, dead and yet still there, still in the house, still in the bubble.

When I was upstairs, I thought I'd feel better downstairs, but I didn't. I walked back and forth, unable to settle down to anything. The sounds kept going on in my head.

At last my father came home from work. He kissed me and said, "Hello, honey, did you take your medicine?"

I'd forgotten, but I said, "Yes, I took it." I had a terrible time, trying to keep my voice sounding all right.

He said, "That's good," and went up the stairs and knocked on Anna's door. He went inside and closed the door, and I stood at the bottom of the stairs hearing the sounds.

When he came down, he said, "Dorrie, I want to talk to you."

I followed him into the living room and we sat in our own chairs, on either side of the fireplace, the way we had done so often before I got sick.

My father leaned back in his chair and closed his eyes, and I thought of how often he had done this just after my mother died.

"Dorrie," he said, "Anna's leaving. She's packed and ready to go."

"It's best, Daddy," I said. "It's best for her to go."

"I talked her into waiting until morning," he said. He opened his eyes and looked at me. "Dorrie," he said, "I don't understand. I don't understand your attitude toward her."

If the sounds hadn't been so much with me, I might have tried to explain. Instead, I sat there, thinking tomorrow she'll be gone. It will be all over. She won't be in the bubble any more.

Anna didn't come downstairs at all that evening. I wanted to fix a good dinner for my father, but I couldn't. I couldn't keep my mind on one thing long enough. I fixed sandwiches and soup and called him to eat. He tried. But he couldn't force much down. I thought, it will be different tomorrow night. With Anna gone, it will be different. I didn't eat either. The anger and the hate and the sounds within me filled me and I wasn't hungry.

I felt as though I were up high someplace where I'd never been before. Nothing was close to me. My father looked as far away as he had when I'd been sick and everyone looked far away.

Finally it was ten o'clock and I said good night to my father. I didn't mind that the evening hadn't gone well, that he'd been distant and silent. Things were going to change. With her gone they would change. I went to my room and undressed and climbed into bed. But I was still high up someplace where there was no sleep.

I don't think I thought of anything while I lay there. I heard my father come upstairs and go into his room. I heard the sound of his shower. I heard his door open and I heard him go to the end of the hall to Anna's room.

I didn't wait very long. He had turned off the hall light, but I found my way. I stood outside her door and listened. For a long time I only heard whispering, but then it changed. The sounds I was hearing were the ones I'd heard coming from my parents' bedroom on Maple Street. He was making love to her.

I wanted to pound on the door and yell, stop it, stop it, stop it, I can't stand it. I can't stand it.

They were killing me. They didn't know it, but they were killing me.

There were the sounds, low at first, and then going higher and higher, and up and up, and then the top and then breaking over and falling down the other side, and then gradually there was silence.

Later my father's voice said, "You're wonderful, darling."

They whispered then, as though they didn't know they'd made any noise before. I couldn't catch what they were saying, but I might have, except the sounds were getting louder in me all the time. Finally I heard them moving around and I crept back down the hall to my room.

I heard my father tiptoe to his room and the house was quiet. There was only the sound of my clock. But in my head there were the sounds, mounting, mounting, getting higher, higher. I heard them over and over, getting higher.

Aunt Helen was going under, going under, sinking in the quicksand. Mrs. Mason walked the edge of the cliff. My mother skied to the right and then to the left and just before I closed my eyes I saw her fall, and then I closed my eyes, but the headache was still terrible.

But when I walked out of my room, the headache was gone, and I was strong and there were no sounds in my head. I made no noise. I was graceful and quiet. I glided down the stairs. I didn't need a light. I knew my way. This way had been laid out for me a long time ago.

In the kitchen I reached to the knife rack over the counter and my hand closed around the bone-handled knife. It belonged in my hand. It felt exactly right. It had always belonged there. My hand and the knife belonged together.

Going up the stairs, I was still graceful and silent. Opening the door of her room, I made no noise. Everything was with me. Everything was with me because what I was doing was right.

I stood by her bed and looked at her, her hair spread out on her pillow, her face smooth and easy, her hand open, waiting. The moon shone into the room on purpose so that I could see her clearly. Everything was with me. There was no hurry. The right end had come.

I stood and let it grow, the sound and the strength. I waited until the strength was so great that I couldn't control it and then the knife flashed up high and down into her. Because of the sound in my head, her scream seemed faint and distant, but it wasn't, and my father was in the room, grabbing me, taking the knife away from me, holding me in a way that had no love to it.

Anna turned on the light and there was blood coming from her shoulder. My father held me at arm's length and looked into my face. And now the distance between us came from his eyes, and it stayed there; it is still there.

I keep telling them they've made a terrible mistake, that my father made a mistake. I don't belong here. The doctors and the nurses are nice and they smile, but they won't listen. I've tried to make them understand how it was.

All I ever wanted was my father.